Fly Fishing
with
MacQuarrie

Fly Fishing
with
MacQuarrie

COMPILED and EDITED by ZACK TAYLOR

WILLOW CREEK PRESS • MINOCQUA, WISCONSIN

Illustrations by Paul Birling

Published in 1995 by Willow Creek Press
P.O. Box 147, Minocqua, WI 54548.

ISBN 1-57223-025-8

Library of Congress Cataloging-in-Publication Data

MacQuarrie, Gordon, d. 1956.
Flyfishing with MacQuarrie / compiled and edited by Zack Taylor.
p. cm.
1. Fly fishing—fiction. 2. Fishing stories, American.
3. Outdoor life—Fiction   I. Taylor, Zack.   II. Title.
PS3563.A3293F58   1995
813'.54—dc20   95-9826
CIP

Printed in the United States of America

*This book is dedicated to all the members of the
Old Duck Hunters' Association who have whiled
away the hours of a May evening in God's cathedral,
otherwise known as a trout stream.*

Contents

Introduction

It is now time for us to go trout fishing with Gordon MacQuarrie. Notice I didn't say fly fishing. The title notwithstanding, these veterans often resorted to the lowly worm or salmon eggs on spinners. Let he who is without sin, etc.

MacQuarrie fished all over North America. But it is no secret he had a special place in his heart for the streams of northern Wisconsin. It was where he grew up, after all. And he liked old things, familiar things to new things. First among equals was the famous Brule. He and his boon companion returned to it again and again. Although there is no brag in the author (Mr. President is something else again), it is apparent that he is a skillful trout fisherman. You'll learn a lot here.

But flies and casts and where big fish lie are secondary to MacQuarrie's essential message. The message is the total appreciation of those days and nights on the streams. Savoring the little things: the "purling" of the river, a bird's joyful song, the feel of current against your back ... little things, what another great outdoor writer calls "Life's

Extras." They are there for all of us. But we must seek them out. With writers like Gordon MacQuarrie to help us, we can.

ZACK TAYLOR

Gordon MacQuarrie

Gordon MacQuarrie was born in Superior, Wisconsin, July 3,1900. He died November 10, 1956 in Milwaukee of a heart attack, his first real illness. He was Scottish in origin, attended Superior State Teachers College and the University of Wisconsin where he received a degree in journalism in 1923.

Upon graduation he joined the Superior Evening Telegram as a reporter and in 1936 became outdoor editor of the Milwaukee Journal. He traveled 40,000 miles a year from Alaska to Key West, Florida. He was a widely read and widely admired reporter on all phases of the outdoors.

He married Helen Peck in 1927. She was the daughter of Al Peck, a Superior auto dealer. Peck became the central character in MacQuarrie's freelance stories. He invented the Old Duck Hunters Association, Inc. (Inc. standing for Incorrigible), made Peck Mr. President or Hizzoner and used him as a glorious foil through which he could inject more humor into his hunting and fish yarns.

When his father-in-law died, the series seemed to die with him. MacQuarrie wrote a story about the joys of being alone, heartbreaking if you know the facts behind the story. Then he meets a grinning man whom he embraces. A new Mr. President takes the helm. The series continues down its glorious path until "The Sickle Man" calls on MacQuarrie himself.

Fish fights. Fights with trout and steelhead. Fish leaping clear of the water, trout boring into hidden holes and forbidden places. Fish soaring downstream with the current under their tails. The incomparable thrill of fishing. Many fights here. Many more to come. This is the MacQuarrie promise.

This story appeared in 1933. When he wrote it MacQuarrie had been married about five years to Hizzoner's daughter. He was growing to love this old man and he introduces him here as a man "who can be ornery without offending." You'll see this friendship deepen and grow as the author develops his character into a loveable curmudgeon; a man with warmth and humor and compassion. A boon companion for life's journey. Who could ask for more? Certainly not Gordon MacQuarrie,

Upstream
Downstream

"I will not go upstream and fish that gin-clear water with a spinner on the first day of any season!" It was Al himself, more or less famous president of the Old Duck Hunters, Inc., speaking, alias Rainbow Al from May 1 to September 1.

"You'd rather sling spinners in the soup down near Lake Superior, then?" I asked.

"My boy," quoth the sage of the North Country, "there are two ways to fish the Brule River in the early season. One is with flies up above, where it's clear; the other is with spinners down below, where it's discolored. The first way you get nothing but a sore wrist from casting. The second way you hook at least one great big fish that may smash your tackle and break your heart. If it's a big rainbow, it's a red-letter day. If it's a big steelhead, it's a red-letter day and you get a stiff wrist to boot."

"Your Honor," said I sorrowfully, "you are a sinful and

wanton fish hog. For several years now you have eschewed the plebian spinner and worms in favor of the aristocratic dry fly in all seasons, and here you are, backsliding like any regenerate after a revival. Where is your sense of decency?"

"The call of the big guy is too strong," replied Al. "I long to spin a spinner in the dark waters of McNeil's pool"

"But think of the fun upstream with flies — especially dry flies."

"Yes, it might be more fun," he admitted reluctantly.

I saw that he was weakening, and pressed on with my best argument — an invitation to visit a friend who had a special road of his own leading in to the upstream waters of the 66-mile river. So we went upstream, but I could see, as we climbed into waders, that he was pessimistic.

Ice still lingered around some cedar tree roots as we invaded the dank river valley. Not very encouraging for a fly fisherman who had hoped for months to try out some new flies and some new, very light opaque leaders. Heavy waders and extra socks inside gave a welcome warmth — until we stepped into the river!

We separated, each to pursue his opening-day luck in the moving flood of ice water. The veteran strode off with resolute steps for some special places downstream, while I waded through a stretch of mud bottom to the current-washed stones of midstream, intending to work upward with dry flies for a while at least.

The shadows on the Brule were pretty long, but the sun

was bright behind the cedars, giving promise of warmth later on. Someone ought to invent waders with fur-lined pockets for early-season fishing. There just isn't any place where one may take the chill out of numbed fingers, unless he folds his arms over his breast and tucks his digits into his armpits — and a fellow must hang on to his rod. The cold penetrated to the marrow, through waders, heavy socks and mackinaw pants. Every so often I was compelled to get out of the water and perch on a rock in Napoleonic pose until circulation was restored sufficiently to permit another go at it.

For a good two hours I fished a 50-yard stretch that invariably produces good browns and rainbows, and not only saw no rises but did not see a sign of a fish in the water. The lingering chill of winter seemed to have laid a killing hand upon the stream, although I knew there should be lots of Lake Superior run rainbows lying in every pool. Search as I would, I could see no sign of any insect life on the water. If the fish saw the Brown Bivisible, plain Coachman and Badger Bivisible that I laid down over them, they gave no sign. I worked with the carefulness of the conscientious early-season practitioner — the way one can apply himself to the tediousness of form is remarkable for the first few trips of the season. But the fish responded not.

When I reached the head of the pool, I retraced my steps and after waiting several minutes again fished upstream with a favorite of mine — a small wet Royal Coachman, well dunked before beginning, and fished as deep as I could get it to go.

But nothing happened, which may be a poor way to start a fishing story but adheres quite strictly to the facts. I did take courage, however, for I am one of those superstitious anglers who feels that the day starts auspiciously when everything doesn't happen all at once. Several river canoes passed me, headed downstream, and I pitied the passengers. Most of them were purple-lipped and shivering as they sat in their boats carried along by the current. One boat came along bearing two anglers who usually take fish, and they told me they had not even seen a fish rise since they started at 4:00 A.M. I felt licked. When those two gentlemen don't get them, not many others do. But it's always darkest just before the dawn.

It was getting warmer. The sun was flooding the valley; and although the lower half of me was congealed, I could take comfort in the upper half being fairly warm. I quit the stream and took to the woods, aiming for a popular spot where the river is divided by an island and the two chutes come together in a fast flow of water. Scores of rainbows had been spawning here a few weeks before. A friend occupied the head of the pool and was going good with a Colorado spinner and angleworms. He had three rainbows. I left him and continued upstream, through the difficult timber that flanks both sides of the Brule. There's one nice thing about that path of the river — there are no paths worn by anglers,

which is in its favor.

The sun had me pretty well thawed out the next time I launched myself into the river, at the lower end of a slow stretch, the head of which is a famous pool. Out over the tail of the pool went the Brown Bivisible, time and again, with no results. Fishermen passing me in canoes occasionally expressed amazement that I should be trying dry flies. I will never forget the satisfaction I experienced when one of them saw my fly sailing by, attached to that new opaque leader. He could not see the leader and asked me if I had not snapped off the fly. If a man could not see it, perhaps a fish could not, either.

I gradually worked up until I was casting over water that must have been five feet deep. When a leader that you had hoped would prove invisible is actually invisible to an old trout hawk, it tends to buoy you up. With more faith in myself and my outfit, I worked the bivisible persistently, carefully, time after time, until my arm ached, and that's hard work if one has neither seen a fish rise or leap. The Brown Bivisible, incidentally, appeals to me as a good fly to use when in doubt — or any other time. There is nothing in insect life like it, but the white twist of hackle dancing over the water enables the angler to see it better.

At that, I believe it would not have been necessary to watch the fly closely in order to hook the fish that finally did rise to it. It was a heavy brown, and never was there a more deliberate, confident attack upon a fly. The fish seemed to have been lying directly beneath it and took it with very little commotion on the surface.

When he felt the line, he dived into the deepest water of the hole, running into the current to do it. A heavy windstorm of last summer had blown a cedar tree into the hole. Part of the tree was still green, its roots clinging tenaciously to the soil, but I knew that a lot of tree was under water right where Mr. Brown was headed for. I put on all the pressure that I dared, and he came out — came out strong, going downstream. He made one glistening leap during which I saw his every spot and then nosed into the bottom in a series of powerful jerks. After that he was mine. I let him play dog in the shallower water, halted a few desperate attempts to get back into the hole with the tree in it, and finally netted him. He measured eighteen inches.

Then I forgot about the cold water entirely! Here were fish that would rise to a fly! Here was opportunity, pleasure, thrill — sport. How glad I was that I had persuaded the honorable Mr. Al to come upstream with me!

Now things were different. Every cast found me looking forward to a rise. Now every inch of the water seemed to give promise of a fish. So does the first fish of the season establish within one that most uncertain of fishermen's foibles — faith — without which no fish are caught and no fun is had.

After a rest of about fifteen minutes, I had begun to retrieve my cast when the second fish shot out from beneath the submerged cedar trees and struck where the fly had been. I saw him as he lifted surfaceward, and my heart beat fast. I know now that I should have waited, but I could not. A few false casts, and the bivisible settled down in the center of the rippling circles where the trout had broken water. My fish had not gone home after the first try. But he started for home the minute he seized the fly, on the next try, and once more I risked the light leader to keep him out of the drowned tree.

I think I had right there as good an opportunity as I ever had to compare the fighting qualities of the brown and the native brook trout. And the native wins over the brown. Attribute it to the colder water if you will, with the explanation that the brookie was more at home there, but this does not satisfy me. The brown was a bigger fish, I learned eventually.

The native proved to be about two inches shorter than the brown; and while he remained under water and fought the dogged, persistent fight of the typical brook trout, it must be recorded the fight was a good one. I did not catch a glimpse of him until he was netted. It is not often nowadays that one can stretch out a fat, 16-inch native squaretail on a rock.

Back at it again I went. It was getting along toward noon, and the occasional canoes passing me headed downstream contained more cheerful passengers. Up in Durant's channel a man had taken two rainbows. In the rips above

Upstream Downstream

Cedar Island another had used a fly effectively on eight nice browns and rainbows, and all along the stream the first-day fiends were reporting things as looking up, with fish rising and a hatch of something or other appearing. More confident than ever, I returned to the fray with a new Brown Bivisible. How I came to love that fly!

I moved around to a glassy slide where the water emptied into the pool. The current here was not fast but much faster than that in the pool, and the work of casting and handling was, therefore, faster and more tiring. I stood so that the fly would alight about twenty feet above where the sharp break of the water occurred and let the fly slide down into the slower water. Faith was bolstered now with past experience, as I knew fish usually lay there, especially toward evening. And it was shallow enough so that a fish would not have to strain his eyesight upward to catch sight of the fly.

The third trout was on and away down the slide, into the pool, before I realized what was happening. He must have known about the drowned cedar tree — but so did I. The leader held him from wrecking me in the tree; so he continued on downstream, and I scrambled after as well as I could, shipping only a little water as I skirted the edge of the pool in record time. He got out of the slower water into faster water, however, and lay broadside to the current, the better to fight the hated line that held him.

I would not have been too sorry if he had beaten me just then, but when I finally netted him I was doubly glad — he was another native just about like the first. Later on he and his kind will have abandoned that part of the stream entirely for the colder holes in the impenetrable swamps far upstream, where in some places the sun's rays never touch the water directly.

I gloated. Two big natives and a brown the first day — and they were just starting to hit dry flies. It was after lunch time, and I returned through the tangled woods to the starting point. In a pool fifty yards below the appointed rendezvous was Al, up to his hips in the stream and working like a nailer, with the sourest expression imaginable on his face. I hardly had the courage to tell him of my luck, but when I did he came snorting out of the river like a disgusted hippo, took down his rod, stowed away his gear and set out for the car.

"Boy," he stated finally, "you and I are going downstream for meat. That is, I'm going downstream. Are you? It's my car, you know."

"But they're hitting dry flies here now. It's warming up."

"They're hitting no dry flies of mine," retaliated the enraged angler. "If I'm going to catch up with those three you have, I've got to make big medicine with a spinner and angleworms. And mark you, all I want is just one chance. Never shall it be said of me that I got licked on the Brule or any other stream because I was too high-hat to use bait."

A fellow can do nothing with a man like that. He got his chance. My anticipation of a glorious afternoon with flies turned to dreary consideration of how far a rainbow can see when the water is as brown as it gets down at McNeil's pool so early in the season. It was not a pleasant drive for me in one sense, for the light of battle was kindled in Al's eye and any mention of my three fish brought prodigious snuffing and snorting and belligerent promises of what he'd do when he got where he wanted to go! The honorable Al can be ornery without actually offending. And he doesn't get licked easily.

"But you're licked today," I badgered him when he pulled up beside the big lone spruce in McNeil's meadow and saw the brown flood of the Brule sweeping by.

"A fish can't even see a spinner in that water," I protested.

"It works both ways, son," retorted the confirmed optimist. "A fish can't see me, either."

In we went, drifting downstream with the current and letting spinners sweep across it before retrieving them. Spring fishing for steelheads and rainbows is the closest thing to salmon fishing that this country affords. The big rainbows from Lake Superior, which begin coming up as soon as the ice-choked mouth of the river is opened, have done as much as anything to make the river famous over the world. Rainbows of ten pounds are not uncommon. Several over twenty pounds in weight have been taken, and the hide of one monster reputed to weigh over twenty-five pounds is tacked on the wall of a restaurant in the town of Brule.

Fly Fishing With MacQuarrie

I was leading the way in the battle of spinners, and I placed my greatest confidence in a long, deep pool about two hundred yards below our starting place — called McNeil's pool by many fishermen. At this part of the river one is not more than three or four miles by river from Lake Superior, and big fish are likely to be caught there the year around. One rainbow about a foot long hit my spinner and shook it free in the first leap. But no matter. There was a pool; and glory be, when I rounded the bend in the river, no one was in it, which was unusual for the opening day.

I worked over the pool for about a half hour before Mr. President caught up with me.

"There's not a fish in it," I remarked. I was mad, of course, at the thought of missing the upstream fishing.

"If there's no fish in that pool, there's no fish in the Brule," he answered. "Therefore, your allegation is a patent falsehood, made with malicious and malevolent intent to destroy the morale of your boon companion."

He doubled up his leader for greater strength, casting funny little glances toward me. I climbed out and sat on the bank in the sun, leaving him to his bitter task. I dislike fishing in murky water, but the faith of my companion is far greater than mine. Maybe that's why he usually catches more fish.

I grew weary of watching his arm go back and then forward to send the spinner searching into every corner of the pool. I lay on my back, shielding my eyes from the sun with my hat, a picture of piscatorial contentment. It was getting on toward four o'clock.

I heard a solid plop, like a log being dropped into the water, which was followed by an involuntary groan from Al. It caused me to sit up. Across the sun-dappled pool I saw him pull his hat down a little more snugly and advance into deeper water. He just looked at me as though he would gladly break my neck for just sitting there and doing nothing. His stubborn lip became more stubborn, if that is possible, and he finally mumbled, "No fish in this pool, eh?"

"Was that a fish that rose?" I asked.

"It was not a fish," he snapped. "It was a crocodile, and it didn't rise, either. It just lifted itself out of the water on its elbows, saw me, and fell back in terror!"

"I hope he bites your leg off."

He declined to answer, but continued the wearying game of shooting his spinner out, letting it ride, then retrieving. The monotony of the thing was maddening. I watched him change from spinner and worms to plain spinner, then plain worms, then salmon eggs and spinner, then — so help me! — spinner with salmon eggs and worms all together. Then he went ashore and dug into his war bag for some little plugs, which he tossed around for what seemed an hour. Finally he let the worms drag on the bottom until he caught a sucker and used a part of the sucker's belly for bait. When that didn't work, he dug still farther into his resources and produced an assortment of bucktail spinners and unnamed creations that were intended originally for bass and pike. By that time he was talking to himself, and I was actually beginning to feel sorry for him. But of such stuff are great fishermen made.

After a while I began feeling sorry for myself. I wanted to get home that day. The conviction began to grow on me that he would never go if he didn't hook the fish. I resumed my siesta on the bank. Something told me he was going to catch the darned fish. He usually did, and I was beginning to feel a little bit licked myself, maybe. I counted about twenty-five of the soft splashes made by his lures as they hit the pool's surface. Then I slept.

"He's on!"

It was a pleasant way to be awakened. I leaped to my feet and began running up and down the bank like an excited retriever. Al's rod was whipping furiously. One jump took the fish — a huge steelhead — about four feet out of water.

There are those who say brother steelhead and brother rainbow are one and the same fish in fighting ability, and there are many who claim that they are the same fish with different coloration. I have never counted the number of scales along their lateral lines. I have never compared their back-bones for a count of vertebrae. I will admit, further, that I can't always tell them apart, but I do know this — that our friend in the pool was a steelhead and, generally speaking, he's a better man than cousin rainbow, which is claiming an awful lot.

Upstream Downstream

There was not a trace of crimson along the sides of the fish. He was out of water enough to show us that. There was no halting this fellow with a five-ounce outfit. When he finished his acrobatics in the air, he plunged into the center of the stream and started off for Lake Superior, with Al stumbling along as best he could and me following with my ridiculous little net. Then back upstream he came and flashed by us, a streak of living green and dim white in the murky water. We went back with him.

"My arm's getting tired, and the rod has creaked a little down near the butt," said Al. "I don't care about the rod, but I'm afraid of the leader. Get your net and try to nail him the next time he goes by!"

There's an assignment for you — try to net a big steelhead, fighting mad, with a little wire-rimmed brook trout net! And another man's fish — perhaps the best fish he will catch that year! I began to wish I had remained asleep.

The fish fell back toward us slowly and rested for a few seconds. Al risked all and horsed him toward me. I knew it was foolish, but I tried it — slipped the net over his torpedo nose and gave a heave shoreward.

All I remember about that was the wire rim of the net bending in my hand as the steelhead, with a single smash that frightened me out of my wits, shot forward and was gone — no, not completely, for when I looked again the rod was whipping madly once more and Al's arm-weariness was showing more plainly than ever in his face. But there was

27

still hope. His lower lip was practically merged with the tip of his nose — I mean Al's lower lip!

"Get my net!" directed Al.

I unharnessed it from his shoulder while he held the steelhead. All the time he was grunting. He grunts like that when he shoots ducks — the only grunting sportsman in captivity.

I stood there with the net like a ninny. More folly, I thought; but Al knew the strength of that leader. I knew that if we lost him I'd catch it, but "orders is orders" in a case like that.

Once more the steelhead was coaxed toward us, and once more I corralled him in the net, with his big tail and half of his body waving in my face. For the second time the net rim bent, but this time we were not so fortunate. The big fellow darted directly between my legs, and in my haste to get out of the way I fell flat on my face in three feet of water. As I scrambled ashore I felt the line entangled about my wader leg, and I had presence of mind enough not to stand up straight and anchor my leg to the bottom, for that would have given the steelhead something solid to pull on.

There was only one thing to do — get ashore on all fours, like a submarine, kicking that leg violently as I went, to free the line. My fly box dropped out of my wader pocket, and I made a dive for it just as I realized the line was free. I caught it and finished the job of swimming ashore.

It was only a miracle that permitted me to disentangle

the line, and Al had the fish fighting the rod again when I brushed the water from my eyes and looked. He was laughing like a maniac, partly at the spectacle I had presented and partly at the relief of knowing that the steelhead was still on. "What'll I do now?" Al called to me.

"Call out the Marines, if you want to," I replied. "I'm not going to let any steelhead drown me."

"He'll just have to tire himself out, and it's all up to the leader," said Al.

Time after time Al worked the steelhead to within five or six feet of him, and the fish was obviously tiring, but closer than that he would not come. The pressure was kept up until he began rolling. He looked like a peeled popple log there in the waning daylight. Then, very carefully and with increasing speed, he was coaxed toward a sandbank. I walked around in back of him to take another dive after him if worst came to worst, but he was worn out after his twenty-minute fight. Al grabbed him quickly by the gills and snaked him ashore. Then we both fell on him!

"What kind of a spinner fetched him out of his hole?" I asked.

For answer Al reached into the steelhead's mouth and pulled out — a long-tailed No. 8 bucktail fly.

"I knew this old mule was down here," he said. "There's always one good one in this pool. He bosses the hole, and if you throw enough stuff at him he's going to get mad finally and come out for a fight."

"Well, we were both right," I said. "But I suppose you would rather have fished here all day."

"Makes no difference to me," the old maestro answered. "I'll get 'em if I get mad enough — upstream or downstream."

And that's no fable.

Here comes some fly fishing at its best. Well, to be honest, we have to throw in some angleworms as well. Lotsa trout. Big trout, one lost, one won. Just great hours on the river. Hours, they say, not deducted from man's allocated span. Satisfying stuff if you're a fisherman.

Go Marengo!

Now in Ashland, Wisconsin, dwells one of the name of Schiller, christened Roy. It was inevitable that the President of the Old Duck Hunters' Association, Inc., and I should one morning, halt our car in front of his house at the hour of 6:30. Though Roy is not a man given to exhortation, he had for some time been pointing and persuading.

"Come," he had said, "to the Marengo River, and I'll show you brown trout in numbers beyond your fondest dreams."

This declaration he repeated from time to time during the winter, despite the fact that Mr. President had tested Roy's ardor by explaining that he was afflicted with nightmares in regard to trout streams and so was inured to the crass realism of disappointment in such matters.

The night previous to our departure from Superior for Ashland, Roy and the Marengo, Mr. President approached me apologetically.

33

Fly Fishing With MacQuarrie

"I'm busy tonight," he had said. "Would you mind digging a few worms for me?"

He said it quickly and then got out of earshot before I could reply. For these many years I have done missionary work with this man and have even won him over to the dry fly for months at a time. Then all of a sudden he backslides — goes on a howling angleworm spree and bobs up for the next trip apologetic but, at heart, unchastened.

There was nothing left to do but dig the worms, thus making me a party to his unregenerate ways. If I waited until just before dark, I could prospect for them in comparative privacy in the old hothouse bed without the neighbors seeing me. Also, a lilac bush screens part of this angleworm ranch: so I was fairly safe. But an urchin passing down the alley on a bicycle betrayed me by yelling: "MacQuarrie's goin' fishin' — he's digging worms!"

One of life's awfullest moments. Me digging worms! I was a fool just to satisfy the whim of Mr. President.

So we picked up Roy at Ashland at the hour when folk were going to early mass. There was about the man Schiller the honest, pungent flavor of citronella — a lingering fragrance which, he explained, remains with him until about August 1, when the mosquitoes aren't so bad. In his hat rim, ringing him like a halo, were sundry flies of his own manufacture, and in his bearing was that air of early-morning confidence I associate with all trout fishermen at 6:30 A.M.

The signs were not auspicious. It had rained over the

whole state that night — the worst rain of the year. With two inches of it had come a knifing wind from Lake Superior which had knocked over a coal-dock, deroofed half a dozen buildings and bashed in scores of windows. Rivers we had passed on the way to Ashland were red torrents, choked with the brick-colored clay of the Lake Superior country. Fish Creek, a famous trout stream four miles out of Ashland, was very high and unbelievably discolored. It was cold, with intermittent dashes of rain and a fog blanket lying just above the earth.

Despite all these things, Roy bore himself with kingly arrogance.

"She'll be high," he admitted, "but she'll be the clearest river in upper Wisconsin today. The Marengo flows through solid granite. I've been there four times this week in the evening after I closed the store. Just smell that basket!"

Confirmatory sniffs of redolent willow withes were made while Roy leaned back and uttered further praise of his favorite river. Our destination was twenty-five miles south of Ashland. Out of the town on highway No. 24, through Sanborn, left at the school, right at the church, and from there on Roy took the wheel. It was easier than yelling from the back seat: "No, don't take that road — the other one!" At that, I believe I could fumble my way back in there with the help of a few settlers. But tell someone on paper how to get there? My only answer to that is that it's the first turn to the left as you enter Wisconsin.

Fly Fishing With MacQuarrie

Like a groom with his bride Roy swept his hand toward the river as we debarked near a narrow bridge. There was the Marengo below us, fifteen or twenty feet wide, studded with granite teeth, overhung with heavy timber, whispering the old, old story of trout, dark pools, conquest — victory! It is necessary to blurt right out here that the Marengo at this point is as beautiful a trout stream as I have ever seen. This is something like heresy to all like myself who fish the famous Brule consistently, but it must be said that the upper Marengo is a stunner.

There she comes — dark, sinuous, fast, cut through a mountain-like formation of granite with here and there igneous rock formations to abrade waders and bump knees. It rises, I am told, in a lake "way up there somewhere — the browns go up there in August to cool off." Then it hastens on downstairs, flows through Lake Marengo, thence into the Bad River, which eventually joins the White River and flows into Lake Superior. Above Lake Marengo, only browns for a long stretch — then specks. Below the lake, nothing but rainbows.

We got our orders from Roy, after first making a fright-ful mess of the interior of the parked car, as is the custom of all trout fishermen. I have striven manfully against this slovenly housekeeping in automobiles on trout streams, but Mr. President prefers the old ways. Once I got him to put everything in a big pack-sack to sort of keep it together. Then he got two pack-sacks to take care of the stuff. But the situation hasn't changed. His stuff just overflows from those sacks. Thus, weeks after a fishing trip, his wife is likely to find a stray leader or even a stray fish in between the rear cushion and the body. This is very bad. Now you take a fish that's been dead a weak or so — but I digress.

Roy was ready first. In fact, I don't think he ever takes his boots off during trout season. He just snapped his rod together and put on a coat which is a completely equipped hardware store.

This part of the Marengo is given to bridges. There are four of them in little more than a mile. All serving little-used roads, too. Roy advised Mr. President to go upstream to bridge number three in order that he might fish downstream as he preferred. He advised me to start where I was and work up, as I had said something about dry flies. As for himself, he went off at a lope downstream from bridge number one.

So I saw Marengo. And while the browns would have none of my floaters that morning, I was continually thrilled by the beauty of the place. At a deep hole Roy had told me about I put on one of his home-made flies, a No. 8 with short-clipped deer-hair body and sparce brown hackle for deep going. In five minutes I had a 12-incher in my net, and before the day was spent I came to bless that dirty white nondescript.

This was the only brown I took as long as I fished upstream. He had a throatful of black beetles and angleworms that bulged out of his mouth as I squeezed him. That should have told me to fish deep, but I am a fool dry-fly fisherman and I have the habit, like many of that ilk, of fishing against the current with a dead fly thrown up and floated down. It just wouldn't work that way — wet or dry.

I turned over trout — maybe fifteen or twenty — and was duly impressed with the number of browns in the river, but they would not take. Three hours or more passed, and the hour of noon drew nigh. Then I met Mr. President. Despite the cold and fog, he was very hot and very bothered.

"I just now began to fish," he cried in accents wild. "What did you guys do — put up a job on me?"

I regarded him with amazement.

"I've been everywhere but here since I left you," he related. "Roy told me to take that road to get to the bridge. I took it, all right. I walked on it until it was just a trail, and still no river. Then I got on another road and walked and walked and walked. (His wading brogues weigh exactly five pounds each!) Every time I crossed a hill I expected to hit the river. I passed through a town, and dogs barked at me. People came out on porches to stare, and one fellow wanted to know what that damn fool was doing with a fish pole fifty miles from a trout stream.

"After a while," he continued wearily, but warming to his subject, "I concluded I was getting close to California and was feeling all right because I know a guy out there who

would have asked me in for a drink. But it struck me suddenly that he was dead and I'd better start back. On the way back I came to a couple of Indian villages — so far back in that the owls flirt with the chickens and the Indians were in native dress. And finally I got back here, and I've just this minute begun to fish!"

Unbelievable but true! The word of Mr. President is gospel. I left him with the injunction to be at the car by one and we would eat, which we did. Roy heard this amazing tale, with variations this time and one alluring chapter in which he encountered two grizzlies and a panther while crossing the Cascades. Roy had four browns like those you see in resort catalogues. Mr. President proceeded to cut a swath through the sandwiches. He had passed up breakfast to hasten the pilgrimage to the Marengo.

"All I had this morning was a factory girl's breakfast," he explained between mouthfuls.

"What's that?" asked Roy.

"A toothpick and a walk."

And to make matters worse, he had fallen in after I had met him.

"So far," he said, "I've fished just about thirty minutes. Yes, she's a nice river, but not for lying down in."

He regarded Roy's four fish with envy, and when we locked up the car for the afternoon attempt he whispered to me, "Where's them worms?"

Roy heard him and yanked a couple of flies from his hat-band. Mr. President accepted them with thanks, but plunged into the duffel in the car to resurrect the lethal can. Then he walked away, muttering to himself.

It should be said, before going farther, that Roy Schiller is the answer to the question: who ties the best flies in Wisconsin? Now Roy is not a commercial fly-tyer and makes no potatoes out of this noble pursuit. He runs his shoe store in Ashland with appropriate devotion and fishes with a rare fire. He is not in the business of tying flies for sale. Such flies as he ties are seldom to be found for sale anywhere. I have known Roy for twenty-five years, and from the time he was a mere dandiprat there have been few to equal him in any undertaking requiring manual dexterity.

Roy fishes any way conditions demand. He is, you will learn on inquiry, just about the top fisherman over Ashland way. He fishes for anything and everything and makes 'em all take artificials. He demonstrates his art at winter clinics sponsored by Sid Gordon, Wisconsin stream ecologist, who, by the way, is doing a good job rebuilding streams in these parts.

The perfection of Roy's art is sufficient to draw wonderment from the most hardened fly-tyers. Some day I should like to enter him in a national competition. He's a guy who does things. As a kid, he could ride a bike better than anybody in the neighborhood and when he wanted anything he made it, from a pair of boots to an automobile. Just one of those incredible mechanical wizards with quick, dexterous hands and a mind to go with them.

"Have it your own way, Mr. President," said Roy. "I like flies, and I know these two will take 'em today."

So Mr. President went away, and Roy went away, and I went away — this time upstream a couple of bridges so that I could fish down. Maybe that would work in that high, foggy river. It did! Reeling in a long line after searching a hole, a pound brown smashed Roy's clipped buck-hair, and what a time I had taking him from under a log! The water was fast, and this one loved home and fireside. I netted him and realized what they wanted was a deep, wet fly — moving. Add up that one, you fishermen who have come to associate the brown with the holy-holy floater or the dead drifting nymph.

I glowed with the pleasure of discovery. Maybe they thought it was a minnow. Or a beetle. Or maybe they knew darned well it was a Schiller fly and just hit it out of revenge.

At the next riffle I dropped it into the very center of the swift water. Oop! Was it a fish or a rock I had snagged? I hauled in the fly. It was still sharp. Back it went again. Wow! It was I who said that when he nailed it again. The hook was set, the tip held high, the slack line permitted to slide through my fingers. Then the slack was gone and he was tearing it off the reel. He was getting too close to a log jam, and I called a halt.

I had forgotten the leader was 4x — that's all. Let it pass. I reeled in and substituted a husky lx of six feet for the 10-

Go Marengo!

foot wisp which I had been using out of dry-fly habit. It was just as good. It was better — it held. The iron-colored Marengo, fast and in flood, required no such finesse as 4x leaders — not even for browns.

Around a bend I came face to face with a Marengo angler who was very busy and who seemed happy. I left the stream and went around him without comment.

I seemed to be on top of fish all afternoon. Trout ten feet away hit me incredibly, but always it was the dirty white buck-hair of Roy's they smashed. At the end of the day a little tube in which I stick used flies, to be gone over later, held a dozen or more flies — not one of which had scratched a fish.

Of course, the river was in flood. The trout were right out in the fastest parts, sometimes in water so strong that it was hard to maintain balance, and what they did to me, and for me, that day will long be remembered. Perhaps I saw or felt forty fish at the Schiller fly. They were cagey about it, but they would at least take a shot at it if I kept it moving against the current. No go on the drift cast. They just let it slide by.

A fluttering movement made them frantic. Time and again they would thrash wildly out of water, striking at the fly two, three and four times — and miss it. Hard to figure it out. Some say they are playing when they do that. I say no. I say, in my new-found wisdom, they've been bottom-feeding, suddenly see what they think is a top-water minnow and rapidly adjust their sights. But no one can make bull's eyes on such short notice. That also accounts, to me, for the fact that they would come back for more — which is not the way I have found Brother Brown on very many afternoons.

They will do the same thing with dry flies. You cast over 'em hard and often. Say you're working over a brown and finally get him interested. Maybe it will take fifty casts. Then he'll try it. But like as not he'll miss. I feel they have to have just so much practice before they become accurate after they suddenly change their mode of feeding. Maybe it's another fool fisherman's fancy. But I've brought 'em up with the "created hatch" idea and had 'em miss it many a time. Of course, on real dry-fly days, when he's looking surface-ward for food, the accuracy of the brown is well known. It's one of the things that makes him such a splendid dry-fly smasher. But skip it if I grow pedantic. I'm running off in a theoretical manner, and there is positively nothing theoretical about the Marengo.

The back cast had to be watched. The roll cast was best in many places, although the Marengo is by no means a creek. Short casts were usually as good as long ones. I wasn't scaring 'em any with my hobnails on the rocks, and the day was very dark, the river high, of course, and fog eddied in and about the deep granite-sided valley. By 7:00 P.M. I had a pocketful of nice brown trout, and not one fish taken was a fingerling. Only one did I put back. They averaged in size over 11 inches. They were fat and dark and hard fighters.

As I neared the bridge where we had landed in the morning I marked a V of water in front of a log jam that divided the current. The Schiller Special was drifted into the V to one side of the jam, then worked back toward me. Even now I can't believe that trout was so big. But he must have been. He came out of the water a clean foot — why, I don't know. The fly wasn't up in the air anywhere. He didn't leap out. He wallowed out — he smashed out. He was one of those shouldery porkers that the kids sometimes get on sucker bait when after big pike in such streams as the Namakagon. Well, I'll put him down at three pounds, being conservative at heart.

I waited a minute. It seemed like years there in the fog; then I repeated the performance. Again he came, in a careening, smashing flop. He didn't touch the fly. At least I didn't feel it either time. What the devil was going on? One more roll cast down in there. Twitch it back. Jerk! Jerk! Jerk! In tantalizing cadence I worked the fly slowly back toward me, and for the third time that awful monster did barrel rolls not twenty feet away from me. Never touched the hook. He was a red and brown dervish in the foggy dusk.

Panic seized me, and I began racing through my pockets for the sinews of war. Bucktails. nymphs, a shiny black beetle, a blue-tinged dragon fly, a spinner (I bow my head in shame!) — all these I tried, but answer cameth not from the

Fly Fishing With MacQuarrie

V in front of the log jam.

It was cold. It was foggy. It was sprinkling rain. My waders had leaked a little that day, and I was damp. I was also worn out from stumbling over granite. But as I left him there in the V and climbed to the bank and the car there was cold sweat on my brow.

If he had taken, I'd have lost him in the logs, no doubt. But he didn't take — yes, he did. He took hold of my throat and the seat of my pants and shook my angler's soul to its foundations. There's always one like that on a stream like the Marengo. I won't forget him, waving his fist under my nose. I quit after that. It was time to quit. A half hour of light remained, but anything else would have been an anti-climax; and further, I can stand having my heart broken only once per day.

Roy arrived at the car as I did. I had eight fish. He had an even dozen, and all of them were big enough to lay on the kitchen sink with a flourish. We lit our pipes to wait for Mr. President, who presently would come and open up the car and let us in to the assorted oddments therein.

In the dying light the fog sifted eerily over the granite, pine-clad bluffs of the Marengo. A whippoorwill abruptly commenced to sing, settling eagerly to his all-night chore. Softly comes the night along the Marengo — even on foggy days.

Then out of the fog and dusk came Mr. President. He groaned with the weight of his gear. Defeat was written on his face. He said nothing until I asked.

"Only a few little ones," he replied with a weary sigh.

He unlocked the doors of the car and began the arduous task of filing away this and that, digging out needful apparel (including my only dry pair of socks) and grunting disapproval at mankind in general. On the other side of the car I saw him fumble awhile after stowing his gear. Then he shouted to us that we could get into the car from his side. We walked around.

My foot slipped on something big and slippery as it touched the running-board. It was a fish. It was a brown trout fish twenty inches long and stretched alongside it were half a dozen others of varying but decent proportions. The revered Mr. President chuckled in the gathering darkness. We fell upon him with a multitude of questions.

"I cannot tell a lie." he finally confessed. "I took him with a gob of worms. He came out twice and smashed a wet fly. Then I reached for the can and put on about five worms — big ones. I dressed that hook as carefully as you'd trim the family Christmas tree. Those worms looked so good I could have eaten them. I let 'er down easy and gentle, once — twice — thrice. Then I worked 'er back, just e-e-e-easy and — there he was!

"Then I reached for my net. Gone, it was! Jerked off in the brush. I held him as long as I could, snaked him toward shore and as he passed me I kicked. It took him amidships. You know I've always said those wading boots of mine are too heavy. They almost killed me this morning, but they saved my life this afternoon. They plowed through the water like a torpedo, and Mr. Trout lit on the shore. Then I lit on top of him, and we wrestled it out. Boy, was he strong — had a hammerlock on me for a minute.

"Just then a wildcat came along, and I jumped on him. Took me nearly five minutes to chase him away, and then — you know how it is — I began looking around for a bear. Just one fightin' mama bear with cubs was what I needed to let the world know how I felt. And if one had come along ..."

There's no use in letting him go on like that. We broke camp and hit the trail through the fog, dropping Roy at Ashland. On the main road back to Superior we got to discussing Roy's flies which, I am bound to repeat, are perfection.

"That boy certainly can tie flies." I declared.

Mr. President peered at me in the dim light from the dash and answered, "I wrap a pretty good angleworm myself."

"Winter done. Waxwings murmuring in the cedars. The Brule sucking around the rocks. Dabs of fog rising here and there. A woodpecker hammering a rampike. The Bois Brule winding at the bottom of its deep valley, saying 'I've got 'em if you're man enough to take 'em from me'." Familiar MacQuarrie music. Along with overboard fish fights and strange maladies that plague Mr. President when there's work to be done.

Hit The Drink

The President of the Old Duck Hunters' Association, Inc., softly closed his back door and came down the steps in the near dark to stow a last armload of gear into the car. A match flared as he relit the battered brier, and from the top of a telephone pole came the triumphant morning music of a robin. "Listen!" the old man whispered.

He got in the seat beside me, closed the car door without slamming it, cranked down a window, and cocked an ear. By the very faint outdoors light and some light from the instrument board I watched Mister President. His eyes crinkled at the corners as the lone robin sang of mysterious and wonderful things in which he would take part on this, the first day of May.

The President whispered: "That guy is the first one up every morning. He gets the tallest pole. Likes to hear himself sing — like a man in a bathtub."

The soloist on the pole was making music from a full

heart and a full stomach. Obviously he sang of a fine world for living in, with acres of lawns and plenty of worms. He seemed carried into ecstasy with the wonder of it all, for at times there was too much music in him to come out of one robin throat. Then he sounded like two robins. This made the Old Man grin all the more.

The singer on the pole still had the stage to himself when I backed the car down the driveway and headed east. Other autos were on the go, all rolling east from the head of Lake Superior to scores of trout streamS which emerge in the north Wisconsin highland and run down to the greatest of fresh-water lakes.

Mister President pulled his old brown mackinaw about him and tended the battered brier.

"That robin on the pole," he mused. "The beggar can sing, but he won't work. You think he helped me dig worms last night? No, sir! He came around after I finished and gobbled up the little ones I left. Ah, dear. When a man's in love he'll stop at nothing."

Daylight built up slowly. There were scores of cars on the road, all of them with trout fishermen, many of them driving a little madly as is the way on opening day. We were in no hurry. Johnny Degerman had reserved our canoe. We passed through sleeping hamlets where windows were lit — more fishermen gulping breakfast.

Beyond the village of Lake Nebagamon we went straight south over a crooked gravel road to Stone's Bridge on the upper Brule River. We were the first at the dock, as Johnny had guessed we would be. He had left a scribbled note on the bow chair of the canoe riding at the downstream end of a flotilla of twenty: "Mac, take this one"

Mister President rigged his rod with the long grip while I loaded the canoe. It was fairly light as we shoved off, but there was no sign of the sun yet. The Brule took charge of the canoe, and we were off, the Old Man's snaky brown line swishing over my head like the call of distant whippoorwills. The Old Duck Hunters' Association fishes this river by ritual: the old Man in the bow chair an hour, I in the stern with pole and paddle; then switch over for the next hour.

There is big magic in this lovely river, and never more than just before sunup of opening day. The brethren who have learned to love this stream will know how it can be.

Winter done. Waxwings murmuring in the cedars. The Brule sucking around the rocks. Dabs of fog rising here and there. A woodpecker hammering a rampike. The Bois Brule winding at the bottom of its deep valley, saying, "I've got 'em if you're man enough to take 'em from me"

We were not out of sight of Stone's Bridge when the Old Man's single wet coachman had found a good native brook about a foot long. It tore out from beneath brush and logs. I netted it and dropped it through the slot in the door of the live-well.

As is often the case on this river, Mister President was plagued with small rainbows. They are pugnacious, under-

sized busters willing to have a go at almost anything offered. These ridiculous midgets, thick in the belly, averaging five to six inches long, grab flies as large as No. 8s, then fling themselves hither and yon, as though they can lick the world and everything in it.

We put the bridge behind us around the first bend and went on down between alders. The stream narrows here to about twenty feet in width, with deep water at the left bank where the alder tips trail. Mister President nailed another native — a typical dark-bodied, red-bellied Brule "speck," not smart like a brown, but bursting with vitality.

A half mile from the bridge we knew the sun was up but

that it would be awhile yet before it crept over the Norways on the high hills to flood the river. Mister President broached an idea; "Let's shove on down fast for two good miles, just in case somebody from the bridge has the same idea."

For half an hour we poled together, putting distance behind and passing up beautiful stretches of fly water. Never mind, there will be plenty of such good water down below. Yet it's not an easy thing to pole when trout are dimpling. Then the hand itches for the feel of cork.

Below the Buckhorn, a luncheon ground marked by antlers nailed to a tree, Mister President went at it again. He feared that no lunker rainbows would be so far upstream. The spawning run had been early. So he retained his light leader.

To be sure, it happened, it always does. In a place where the Brule spreads out over washed gravel, a rainbow of about four pounds offered battle. It was all over in something like six seconds. The fish shot off the shoal to deep water, plunged downstream in the main current — and that's all there was to it.

"Somebody in this organization," Mister President wailed, "had ought to fine me about $10,000."

"Put on a leader. There are a few big ones here anyway. I know a place."

He rerigged while I poled to the next likely spot for a big one. Brule rainbows are great ones for lying over gravel beds in pretty swift current. I have seen scores of them lying so, up to 10 pounds and better, in areas so restricted that they scrap among themselves for elbow-room.

The Old Man dug up a bass leader and with a dark bass-sized bucktail, good Brule medicine on big fish, flailed the water. He failed to get a roll and his hour was up, so we exchanged places. I was using Mr. President's outfit. He let the canoe work down to the end of this gravel bed.

Wham! A fine word, that for rainbows. This fellow did as all smart rainbows do — work into the current, lie in it crosswise, then jerk, jerk, jerk! They have plenty of power and they know how to let the current add to it. I pinned my hopes on that bass leader. When the fish broke, he looked pretty good, deep in the middle. As soon as Mister President saw him he ordered: "Hit the drink!"

Overboard the water was cold as sin. The Old Man knew what he was doing when he shouted that advice. He knew that a wading fisherman had more maneuverability than one in the most skillfully handled boat. The rainbow took me downstream about fifty yards. Once off the gravel bed there were holes to contend with, some of them right against the bank. Sometimes I got through them only by hanging to cedar boughs. Mister President followed in the canoe.

The rainbow gave me hell in more ways than one. Not the least of it was the cold of the river. The fish just decided: "If you're going to fight me, you do it on my home grounds."

When the jerking had subsided, I heard a splashing behind me. It was the Old Man in there with me, belly-deep. No waders. He was busy unwinding the white cotton mesh of a four-foot net as he waded below me and below the sulking fish. He did not miss on the first pass. Slabsides went to his destiny in the long white meshes.

The two of us got ashore and made a fire. We had to open the live-well cover to put the big rainbow inside. He was too much fish to go through the slot. We stripped before the fire and dried out. The sun had finally found the bottom of the valley. It felt mighty good. We boiled coffee and fried the two brookies.

If you ever get to fish the Brule, bring along a little bacon, some fresh home-made bread and a chunk of butter. And a frying pan.

It came Mister President's turn to regain the bow chair. The sun was high and the day warm. He returned to a light leader and small wet flies. Under such conditions he swears by such as Cowdungs, Hare's Ears, Brown Hackles.

He picked up some small native and a few fly-weight rainbows, and so did I when it came my turn to ride the prow chair. These went into the live-well where Slabsides announced his living presence every whipstitch by banging his prison wall with a broad tail. It's good to hear them thump like that.

After the noon hour Mister President announced, "We'll

go ashore here."

The Old Duck Hunters always go ashore at this place, which is May's Rips, six miles downstream from the put-in bridge. It's a place where the Brule is beginning to feel its oats and starting to make some downhill jumps on its way to Gitche Gumee.

"I can eat 'em twice a day, and then some," said Mister President, busy with the skillet.

We dried our clothes some more. We spread a couple of blankets on a cedar knoll and lazily watched other canoes, with other fishermen, come down the waters which we had explored first in the season. We listened to the croaks of wheeling ravens and the talk of the river elbowing down through May's Rips, and also we listened to the dear music of the white throated sparrow, which sounds so sad and makes trout fishermen so happy.

We dozed. Mister President was snoring when I awoke. He aroused slowly.

"Dammit!" he said. "I got a crick in my left shoulder. Dunno as I'll be much good poling back upstream."

There was evidence that the three hours of repose had stiffened his shoulder. It seemed the ground damp had come right up though the blanket.

"But my right shoulder's all right," he observed.

"You can swing a fly rod?"

"It'll hurt, but I can do it."

I took over the poling and he seized the bamboo scepter

and moved in to the throne in the bow. Now it was upstream fishing with floating flies. The time of day was excellent for such business. It had been warm enough to produce a sustained hatch of gray-blue fliers, lots of them. A brown bivisible, size 12, did the trick. A good number of pan-warmers joined Slabsides in his captivity in the live-well.

"But there ain't much to show the neighbors except that rainbow," Mister President pointed out.

In one still, deep pool the Old Man bit through the gut, stuck the floater in his hat-band and dunked with worms shamelessly and successfully for browns which would not surface. He took three. One, he insisted, would "go pound and a half on our butcher's scale."

Upper Brule browns in those deep holes are challengers. There are plenty of them, all very sharp-witted, or cautious, which amounts to the same thing for a fish. Given a dark, warm, windy day over these holes, a man has a fair chance to show them who's boss. On 'most any other kind of day they just lie there and snicker at you.

The shadows of the cedars on the river stretched out. Clouds riding a southwest wind formed blackly. Nighthawks swooped. It would rain before we made Stone's Bridge. Mister President put on his mackinaw and kept fishing. The rain stabbed violently at the Brule.

In ten minutes it was over and the nighthawks were diving once more. The sun came out strong. A porky swam the stream, floating high. The rain made everything smell good. Mister President loosened the single button on his mackinaw and shook it to throw off the rain drops. He said, "My left shoulder is pretty creaky."

I poled on upstream and he dozed in the sun. From my place in the stern I could see more of the gray of his hair as his head fell forward. Slabsides thumped in the live-well.

My hand itched for cork, as fish were rising. But it would not be the right thing to wake up the Old Man. The Old Duck Hunters' junior membership opposes such nonsense.

There is a place about a mile and a half below Stone's Bridge where the Brule twists and narrows among rocks and captured logs and brush. It was here where the itching rod hand became too much to ignore. I crawled forward and got the rod, crawled back to the stern and worked paddle and rod together, which takes some doing, unless you are of a piece with some Brule guides, which I am not.

A good fish was feeding boldly on the left bank, right under the brush. I managed to keep the canoe in position long enough to lay one good one in the right spot above him. It floated down. He just walked over and sucked it in. I dropped the paddle and let the canoe do what it would.

That brown was not more than a two-pounder. But he put a set in the rod on his first dash. It is not easy to handle a canoe and a brown at once in quick current. Luck and good tackle held him. He went under the canoe and then downstream while the canoe yawed in the current.

Hit The Drink

"Hit the drink!" It was the Old Man, suddenly awake, yelling good advice again. In I went. The water seemed just as cold. And downstream went Mister Brown to a snaggy hole below a small rapids.

This time the President of the Old Duck Hunters' Association did not join me. He did the entire job of coaching from the bow-chair throne.

Sometimes he cussed a little, as when I let the fish get in under the bank. He hung on to cedar branches to keep the canoe from drifting down on top of the battle. Then he flung the net to me, and I grabbed its floating wood handle as it went by.

So eventually I came dripping back into the canoe with a nice fish and a badly set tip joint on a grand old trout rod. Mister President had the cover of the live-well wide open for me. He looked in on the welter of trout there. Then he took out his "gold watch and chain" and noted the time. He said we could just make it back to Stone's Bridge before dark if he poled — in the stern.

Unloading at the bridge I asked him, "How come you could pole up a mile and a half of current with that sore shoulder?"

"Sore shoulder? Oh, that. Funny the way them aches and pains come and go."

This yarn was published in 1934. In it you see the author creating the character of Mr. President. He appears here as "The Fellow I Often Fish With" or simply as, "The Other Fellow." MacQuarrie probably didn't realize it but his father-in-law's buffoonery and wonderful zest for life was molding the writer. In the early stages MacQuarrie stands up to the old man. As the series matured MacQuarrie gladly accepts second place and holds Hizzonor in quiet deference ... most of the time.

One more thing. Trout Town is one heck of a fishing story. What fisherman hasn't had a day or night when everything goes right? And who can entirely keep their wits about them at such times? "I am a feckless fool, a-tremble with anticipation and utterly unable to be cool, calm and collected."

Trout
Town

Trout Town comes alive at sundown. From beneath over-hanging banks, sunken logs and sheltering rocks come the adult citizenry to chase the dandiprats out of the riffles and accept whatever hatch the evening has to offer.

This is the witching hour for the dry fly angler. He wipes his hot forehead with kerchief about his neck, lights a fresh bowl of tobacco, looks well to his terminal tackle, and so is prepared for the day's denouement.

It is truly the magic hour. A favorite fly is selected. It may be a hideous No. 6 Jungle Cock or a dapper No. 14 Pink Lady. The fly is knotted on. The angler advances to the tail of his pool. The somber curtain of night creeps up in the east. The knotted fly is held up to the light of the west to make sure that all is well—and the play begins.

Then the little "slaps" of playful six-inchers give way to businesslike "ker-plunks" as more powerful tails hit the surface. A street of water, during the midday seemingly as empty as a deserted city, becomes an avenue of fish life, with its inhabitants eager for the evening hatch — and maybe the angler's fly.

We've all been there. We know the hour, the day, the pool. And it is the very staff of life to an angler.

I just got back from Trout Town. It was three nights ago, but the memory of it has been with me ever since. I can still see the Brule, lifeless except for small fish, become suddenly quiet, as though resting from the day's work of running down to Lake Superior. I can still see the shower of brownish flies that seemed to come from nowhere. I can still see the first good brown trout shoulder his way to the surface.

Here are furtive beauty, dynamic life, wild courage. Here is a place to test the sureness of a trembling hand. Here is opportunity to match one's beloved enemy on his own terms, taking the bitter with the sweet and victories with defeats. Here, if anywhere, a fisherman looks up at the sky and down at the stream and thanks his gods for being a fisherman.

The Fellow I Often Fish With was with me that evening. Throughout the sizzling afternoon we had conspired and perspired to ensnare brother trout from his cool retreat in the bottom of the river. We might just as well have rested beneath the pines and saved our strength, but the Other Fellow is not made of such stuff. "If they're hard to get, they're more fun getting," he avowed about two hours after we had started, with little to show.

Trout Town

Each of us had a couple of small rainbows. I was counting heavily on the business of the evening, and I knew that he, too, had this in mind.

"Let's take a rest until it cools off," I suggested. "It's obvious there's nothing doing. There probably will be later on."

"Young man," he young-manned, "you still have much to learn of the ways of trout. There remains before you at least one big lesson in moral sacrifice that, I am sorry to say, you have not learned yourself. You must realize that trout fishing is a pilgrimage of the spirit — a test of what character you still possess after fishing with me. It is a game in which you give much to gain much.

"I have always found that he who suffers in the bright sun will often reap his reward at dusk. But I have found, too, that he who lolls in the shade during the working hours, or the time of penance, as it were, generally receives no such rich evening reward. Maybe it is because I am superstitious, but I have no mortal use for a fisherman who will try to reap the pleasures of the evening rise without first having prepared his soul and humbled himself by ceaseless effort when the fish riseth not."

"Well spoken, Sir Izaak!" I applauded. "I shall remain by thy side in this fishless river, though we never see a trout, or feel its pull, even unto the end of this day's fishing."

So I stayed, and made a virtue of a necessity, for he had my cigarettes and wouldn't give them back. Furthermore, he had my evening lunch in his fishing pocket. He usually sees to it that things are arranged that way.

But the hot day passed — and even on a hot day, when trout are listless, there are things to do if one will look around. The birds are always on hand, and the queer lights and shadows on the trees, especially the spruces, are worthy of a passing glance. On the side of a spruce where the sun strikes there is a smile, and the tree is positively gloomy on the shady side. I have a speaking acquaintance with several splendid spruce trees of great character and individuality along the Brule. There are also fish places to look for and bottoms to explore — knowledge to be filed away in the mind for future reference. And there is, above all, the anticipation of something better later in the day.

I had a wonderful experience that night. I have seen hundreds of rises on many waters. On the Namakagon I have seen browns, at high noon, start feeding suddenly, with no sign of a hatch, continue for twenty minutes or so, and stop just as suddenly as they started. On the Iron I have seen water, the surface of which was devoid of all signs of a rise, yield twelve or fourteen big trout within an hour. And on the Brule there is always a trout turnout sometime during the day. It may be fair, good or poor, but always something. That's why so many anglers go back to it again and again.

I am sure my experience was unusual, even if it were only because I had not had such an experience before. Others may have — perhaps all anglers have had many similar days.

The sun retreated behind the spruce steeples, and I got

ready. The Other Fellow was upstream 200 yards. We fish too fast on the Brule, we dry-fly fellows, and I had planned to overtake him within a few minutes; but as things turned out, I did not see him until near dark.

Now, about 150 yards below the ranger's cabin in the state park, outside the town of Brule, there is a 100-yard stretch of beautiful water, shallow in the middle and deeper at both banks, especially the right bank. You stand in the shallower water and work the deep water easily. And if you are careful, you don't forget the shallow directly ahead of you and maybe a little to the right. Sometimes it yields surprising fish.

I was halfway up this wide, comparatively slow stretch, to the point where a 75-foot spruce sticks out from the right bank over the river. This tree spreads over a fairly fast run, and just below and above are deep pools. All along the bank there are dense bushes and old logs rooted into the bank, the bank itself being concave. The browns just love it. There was a small brown fly showing, and I grabbed one. Just a little dusty brown fellow to me, but he indicated a Brown Bivisible, which is my favorite fly anyway. Some day I shall buy a big book with colored plates and scientific descriptions of flies, and will plan, carefully and cautiously, to learn how to imitate the hatch on the water. Some day, I say, I shall do that, and I will know the names of the flies, too. But I know that when the hour of dusk has come and there is a fish to be caught, lying in the riffles ahead of me, I will tie on a No. 12 Brown Bivisible and mark myself forevermore as an unprincipled opportunist, clinging with superstitious weakness to the past.

Some day I shall try something else. And some day, too, I shall learn how to tie a double water knot so that I may fasten broken or shortened leaders together and thus confound all anglers who knoweth not how to tie a double water knot. Yes, yes; no doubt, no doubt ...

The browns were ravenous. Can more be said? I have never seen anything like it — yes, I have, on private ponds and one night, years ago, before I began fishing for trout. Now I know they were trout, because I know there are millions of trout in the Brule.

The next day I told two men about it. I was pretty much fired by my experience. One of them was an old hand at the dry fly game. The other was a lake fisherman — and a good one — who has his first-day fling at the Brule annually, gets nothing, year in and year out, and then quits cold. After hearing my story that "it looked like it was raining," the lake fisherman suggested an examination by an alienist. The veteran of the floating fly smiled. He knew all about that kind of thing. To him I told it all.

I tried the lower pool — right at the place where the dark water slides out from beneath the spruce-tree branches. Had I been wise, I should have worked the tail of the pool, but I am not wise under such circumstances. I am a feckless fool, a-tremble with anticipation and utterly unable to be cool, calm and collected. The hungry browns were brimming over the upper end of the pool, and there I went.

One forgets himself more completely, at such a time, than at any other moment of his life. I was no longer a person with a rod, a reel, a line, a leader and a fly, all hitched together. I became, with my paraphernalia, a single, purposeful unit.

The first cast fell short of the overhanging branches, and the fly was wafted to the dark water. I could see it well in the falling light, its white neck of hackle looming like a little lighthouse. It floated three or four feet and then disappeared. No impulsive rush, no flash of fish, no slap of tail. That fish knew his business. A little fly — he would not bother to exert himself too much for it. I set the hook, and he was on with a strong, sudden wiggle that told me I need not implant the hook more firmly.

Into the bank he went, away from the channel where he had been feeding. Away from the dinner table and under a mass of brush and driftwood. I horsed him out and backed into midstream as quietly as possible, trying not to disturb the place more than necessary. The trout did not break water until I had him in the middle of the river, when he thrashed vigorously as I tried to bring him to net. He was a brown. I knew that by his fight — dogged, persistent, cagey, but lacking the brilliant madness of the fight a hooked rainbow makes. One can gauge the fight of a brown, but never that of a rainbow. I netted him. He was a good foot long.

Fly Fishing With MacQuarrie

The matted fly was whipped dry and sent forth again, to the same spot. Fish were rising there as though nothing had happened, and one was coming upward with the persistency of a fiddling cricket. The fearlessness of the trout that evening was something I had never seen before. The steadily feeding brown would show his entire body in his rise, but made little commotion. Over him I floated the fly, time and again, and though he kept feeding he paid no heed to the artificial. Several times he rose when the fly was not a foot from him. I finally quit him, fearing to lose other chances.

I tried to the right of the pool, in water a little shallower. A smaller fish was taken there. A few minutes later, thinking to rest the head of the pool, I dropped the fly in the shallower water of midstream, directly in front of me. It was taken immediately, and this third trout was nearly as large as the first — all browns. Three without moving very far from one spot.

I was doing famously; so I returned to the cagey one that was so particular about his supper. He had been feeding all the time I caught the other two. On my previous trials I had cast the fly about five feet ahead of him and had let it drift down. This time, on an impulse, I let it drop as close to his dining table as I could, and it came down in the right place with a little splat. He grabbed it two seconds after it struck. and was off to the concave bank. The same old story — he was persuaded to come out into the middle of the stream — and there I ran him ragged.

Trout Town

Further effort at that spot failed. But I felt that the pool above would be as good or better. Perhaps there were six or eight good fish rising in that pool. Maybe more. Now I was more careful, and more confident. I was beginning to feel I had the situation pretty well in hand. I took a couple of 10-inchers out of the tail of the pool, fought them away from the bank and creeled them without disturbing the other feeding fish in the least.

I have yet no explanation for the indifference of the browns to my presence that night. They must have seen me. I can only conclude that they had spent a warm day on the bottom of the stream and were making up for lost time by particularly heavy feeding.

One energetic fish occupied the center of the pool, and I tried for him. He took the fly without much fuss, but I knew his pedigree the minute he did — a rainbow.

Have you ever attended a prize-fight and sat, listless, through three of four tame preliminaries, then awaited the final bout with melancholy forebodings? Maybe the man next to you has told you that the whole card has been framed. You look around for your hat and coat and begin to wonder where you parked your car. Then, under the glow of the floodlights, two demons incarnate are unleashed and you lean forward, like the savage you are, and howl with the mob for a knock-out.

That rainbow made me lean forward and howl for a knock-out. For a split second he did not know what he had, and then he went crazy. He leaped once, and two seconds later leaped again, twenty feet downstream, on a slack line.

One does nothing with a hooked rainbow for about thirty seconds. The rainbow has everything his way. He was all over the pool, under the bank, out in the open, and back to his pool before I felt I had a chance to net him. When he had settled down, I slowly worked him toward me, stripping in line. I looked for a bigger fish than the first brown. He was hardly as big — but what a fighter!

The Other Fellow came splashing downstream to me. He was getting ready to quit. By his swagger I knew he had caught fish. I asked him to avoid the pool, and he made a long detour, coming up in back of me. He had seven, browns and rainbows, and he was a happy man. I asked him, a veteran of many a trout season, if he had ever seen such a rise. He said he had, but not often. As we spoke a fish rose almost at my knee. They were everywhere — fearless and greedy.

While he stood there I tossed the fly into the far corner of the head of the pool, near a bush that hung out over the river. It was getting darker, and I thought the fly had landed in the bush. I gave a tentative pull, and the fly remained wherever it was. A more vigorous pull, then a jerk, and I got an answering jerk that was a complete surprise. Three more jerks came out of the bush, and in my eagerness I jerked too hard. Fly, leader and line came back to me and were tangled almost inextricably.

Trout Town

"That was a fish," I said as calmly as I could.

"Looked to me like you were stuck in a tree," said the Other Fellow.

He lit matches in order to help me untangle the snarl, but it was of no use. I told him to try the pool, not omitting the corner, while I retreated to a rock, where I sat down and rigged up anew. It took me fully twenty minutes in the half light, and while I did so the Other Fellow took a couple of little rainbows from the pool. I knew that he had not disturbed the corner, and that he felt I had actually been snagged on a bush. He marched off upstream, telling me he would wait ten minutes for me just above the pool.

I approached within range of the corner with a profound respect for whatever was in it. In place of the minute bivisible, I had attached a No. 8 nondescript with white body and brown hackle, a good juicy mouthful of a fly. I did not bother to oil it, as it was almost dark and I planned to keep it dry for what little fishing remained by whipping it.

The first cast did the trick. I measured out enough line barely to miss the bush. A rush and splash, and I had hold of the river bottom. The fish leaped and writhed. I could barely see him, but he looked big and felt bigger. I guessed him to be another rainbow — maybe a two-pounder. I am convinced he was the same fish I had on before and was highly pleased with myself. My plan was working well, though I have realized since that it was pure luck that my outfit had become snarled, else I would have rushed him

73

with another offering and might have scared him away.

I took him out of the pool, gradually, and got him into the center of the stream. There was no horsing this fellow. He had to be cajoled. Once he got back under the bank, but luck was with me and I took him away from that dangerous place. Then he went downstream, and I followed, not wishing to pay out line in the gathering darkness. I kept him as close to me as I could. I wondered if my little net would hold him and looked for a sand beach where I might land him. There was none. It must be the net or nothing. I worked him in front of me and then let him drift down toward me. The first sweep of the net did the trick, and I lifted him out of the water.

Curled up in the net, his nose and tail just barely missed touching the rim. No more fishing now. Occasional "ker-plunks" told me the fish were still feeding, but the day was over. The Brule had been more than kind to me, and I was anxious to show the Other Fellow what had been lying in that corner.

I found him above me, at a place where the river makes a little island, and in the weak light I held up my big trout. It didn't have to be very light to see that fellow. He was big enough to loom in the most meager light. The fish measured about 20 inches, perhaps a little more. He was a dark-hued brown, and may have weighed from two to two and a quarter pounds.

"There, mister," said I, "is the fish I told you was in that

Trout Town

corner. And you passed him up for a couple of little ones.
You'll listen to me next time."

"Gosh, that is a nice fish," he replied.

"He'll go a half pound — easy!"

Here comes another of the mighty MacQuarrie themes. The outdoors, a river, can cure you. It can restore a man's soul. A man had a nervous breakdown when he came to the river in spring. By September he "had the color and zest of a wild Indian. Old Doc Brule cured him."

Sure it did. The man was probably depressed. The man lived in his trailer and the sound of the river was a constant in his ears. He caught trout. His cares faded. In four months "old Doc Brule" had him fit again.

Why wouldn't it? Why wouldn't the spectacle of two grown men pausing to enjoy the sound of a white-throated sparrow singing? Reveling in such small ecstasies of nature can take a long leap toward keeping a soul intact. You think MacQuarrie didn't know this? He invented it!

From downriver there came "the song of eternal sweetness as a sleepy white-throat gave his final benediction to the day."

When The White-Throats Sing

"Mebbe," said the President of the Old Duck Hunters' Association, "I am all wrong, but I think I'm right!"

We had been sitting in front of his place of business, arguing about when trout hit best. To climax an hour or more of wrangling he had said, "They do best for me when the white-throats sing."

I asked why.

"Because that's when I think they'll hit."

There is nothing to be done about a man like that. Though heavily freighted with the science of trout, he will toss it out the window to play a hunch.

Homeward-bound, I had come by his business place and spied him in a new car in the showroom. I was intent on the brisk walk ahead, and my mind was made up. I would just hike along smartly and be gone with a wave of the hand.

Fly Fishing With MacQuarrie

I saw his brown eyes following me. I tried to get by, but he let out a "Hey!" that went right through the showroom windows. And there I was in the car beside him, meek as any house dog.

The conversation went through wet flies, dry flies, soft rod, stiff rod, early season, late season — right down to the strange rainbow run up north Wisconsin's Brule, of which so little is known. I had done most of the talking when the palaver was confined to, shall we say, theory. Only along toward the meatier portions of the conference did he speak up. Then, flicking cigar ashes, he had announced: "They'll hit when the white-throats sing."

"I must be getting on," I said.

"Just sit there and wait," he said. "I'll be leaving for home pretty soon."

I sat, even though "pretty soon" to the President of the Old Duck Hunters may be in the next five minutes or next January. His knack for getting people to wait for him amounts to genius.

It was well-nigh two hours after the legal time of 6 P.M. when we drove to my door. Two hours devoted to rambling and heated discourse on trout.

He called for me the next mid-afternoon, and we headed for the river that strikes down from Douglas County, Wisconsin, to Lake Superior.

It was one of those May days. It might have snowed. But it was 75 above. Lilacs were in blossom. The sky was blue and bland. The air reeked with earth smells.

Mister President wheeled through Lake Nebagamon and east along the county trunk. Thence across the iron bridge over the Brule to the trivial, barely visible road that bears north — past a logs-on-end house. Down this road he let the car nose its own way in the ruts, not even getting out to chop away down-stuff, but just driving through with many a crunch of limbs against metal. The farther you go on this road the closer the brush crowds it.

There is a little turn-around at the end of this road. If you cramp the wheels sharply enough, you can swing around and face out — a great help after dark. There is also a rough board table handy for leaning a rod against. And, best of all, there is at this place a grand dull roar, caused by the Brule running downhill through boulders. A fisherman would know what it meant the first time.

Men who know me will tell you that I am inclined to reckless haste in any campaign on this stream. They will tell you that I practically fall apart spiritually once I am within earshot of the Brule. And that I have been known to go to it so recklessly as to step into it without remembering that I took off my trousers — but forgot to put on waders.

It is so. I irked Mister President with my unseemly haste, for he sat and declared: "Look here. When I come to fish the Brule above the stone dam, I do not wish to be waited on by a committee for the local drive. I do not wish anyone to try and sell me anything. I do not want to buy a set of the

79

Fly Fishing With MacQuarrie

Encyclopedia Universillia, or a patent can opener, or a new kind of potato peeler. I will not be driven to this river like a mule. Nor will I leap into it like a damn bullfrog!"

Deliberately he drew on waders. Deliberately he strung up the rod with the 16-inch cork grip — an invention long neglected by rod makers. He forced me to sit while he checked pockets for the sinews of war, turned the key in the car and finally announced, "Now!"

Even then he did not plunge headlong down the steep path. He stood and listened where the path dipped sharply. At first, all I heard was the keener roar of the river. Then he squeezed my arm, and above the roar of the river I heard it! Somewhere down in that trough a white-throat sang. He must have been a way downstream, but it is hard to say. It was the sad, brave salute of the wilderness sparrow for the place on earth he loved the best. It rose at intervals from the deep valley. Some parts of it would be lost in the singing river, and some parts of it would rise triumphantly in the air and come strongly to our ears.

"Ain't he a guy?" said Mister President, chuckling.

Mere words cannot make that picture live again. Nor can words duplicate the sounds, the smells, the very tastes of the Brule valley in May.

Each time the bird sang, Mister President would squeeze my arm. Then, if ever, I saw deep into this old and good man, Mister President, so keenly tuned to the real life about him.

When The White-Throats Sings

"The little beggar," he said softly. "Once I kept one in my back yard for a week with bread crumbs and seeds. Thought he'd stay and build a home. Not him! Never yet was a white-throat didn't know a trout stream was the best place on earth to live."

The Old Duck Hunters parted there. I was a long time pondering the music, thinking of those who said he sang "Poor Canada ... Canada ... Canada." And of those who said he was really saying "Peabody ... Peabody ... Peabody." So do men fight to claim this mite of feathers for their own, and why not? Music like his has never been matched for simple beauty.

I wet my waders in the Brule. Many times have the Old Duck Hunters come to this place. You might say that such places never change, that the same old boulders and turns and banks are everlasting in one man's life. It is a lie to say that. Such places change as much as friends, as much as hunting dogs, as much as sunsets, or as much as spring, which is never quite the same, praise be.

This is good water. The hasty man does not know it well. He does not know of the straight-north road from east of the Winnebojou bridge. The hasty man knows much of the Brule State Park camp just below this stretch — below the the old stone dam. The hasty man has no business on a trout stream, anyway; so why fret about him?

Once I knew a man beset with business cares who came to the little turn-around at the end of this road and camped

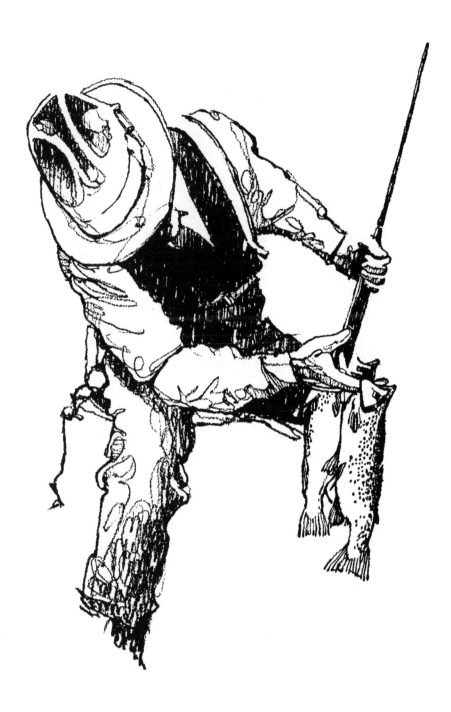

for three months in a trailer. He was as happy a man as I ever knew. He caught up with himself there.

He had a danged old five-dollar rod that I borrowed once. He had his trailer backed under a tall pine. He had a nervous breakdown when he arrived in the spring, and he had the color and zest of a wild Indian when he left in September.

Old Doc Brule cured him. He went to sleep to the river's lullaby and woke up to the song of its birds. He built himself back by slogging up and down the Brule's rocky backbone. He caught and ate more trout than mortal man is entitled to these days. He looks back to it today as his second boyhood.

Letting myself down that watery stairway, I thought of him. Of how lucky he had been to find this place. Of the danged old rod he owned which drove me to distraction that day I broke mine. Of the books he had read in that pine-shaded trailer and how, every time I saw him, he was browner and tougher, and grinned wider and wider.

The river was in splendid order that afternoon. Within the week it had rained very hard, such a rain as would raise the average river to a terrific stage. The Brule was up about two inches; that was all. The Brule is never apoplectic. Down below the town of Brule it may run a bit red where rains sluice off clay banks. But never does it grow dirty up there above the stone dam — never. Where are streams like that this day?

Fly Fishing With MacQuarrie

My fly was a Jock Scott of trout proportions and salmon-fly construction, an item right difficult to get nowadays. The first fish it turned was a thoughtful brown which investigated but did not touch. It merely rose, bowed and vanished in the wings.

Very well. The afternoon was young. Two hours later that spotted gentleman would feel differently. There'd be a brash rainbow or brookie somewhere soon. Especially would there be a native if I could work that gaudy little soaker over into the right bank where there was a cool drip from the hillside and some rocks to hold the coolness before it oozed away in the current.

The cool spot fooled me. No native came forth, but rather a tough rainbow — ten inches of solid muscle, fighting in the current before his doorstep like a two-pounder. He was netted. There must be a local boy, a true native son of the Brule in that rocky cool spot. Must be ...

A lucky first cast put the Scotsman close in against the edge of rocks, where the spring water dribbled down from the bank. The water was quiet there, and by virtue of a slack line the fly stood stock-still. "That fatal pause," the President has always called it when a fly lingers miraculously in slack water, though on the verge of swift water.

The brookie took it with the joyous abandon of his kind — an abandon which the Old Duck Hunters long ago agreed among themselves is one good reason for his scarcity. Let the men of trout look into this a bit. Warming water is indeed one answer. Gullibility is another, but you seldom hear it mentioned. My brookie was a bit bigger than the rainbow, a purplish fellow, but in no wise as darkly radiant as his cousins fifteen miles upstream that spend their days beneath the alders and feed principally on insects.

In the fast water of this part of the Brule there are some deep holes. They lie behind stubborn boulders. It is well to hug the shore while wading here. One wrong step, and the river just reaches up and takes a man in. Sometimes, before spitting him out, the Brule will fetch him along twenty or thirty feet, bumpily and abrasively. A friend of mine invariably refers to one good rip here as "the place where I swim the Brule every time I wade it."

Some of the elderly faithful will tackle this stretch only out of a canoe, such as might be piloted by those old Brule familiars: Carl Miller, Johnny Degerman, or John LaRock. Indeed, there are times when the stoutest wading men would prefer to be seated in the fore end of a canoe, knowing that their fate was in the hands of a stalwart abaft wielding a 12-foot spruce pole shod with steel.

Mister President, though long since qualified for such delightfully easy fishing, has a]ways insisted upon working this stretch standing on his own two legs. He likes to come to terms with a river.

Back of one of those big boulders I met the inevitable. The river bottom betrayed me. Where I thought there had been solid bottom there was only water. The casual reader of this screed need not be perturbed. My fate was certain, but not serious. The river grabbed me by the seat of the pants, kicked me along about ten feet and sloshed me gently into the side of another boulder. I went ashore and peeled.

It was two hours to sunset. I built a fire, more smudge than flames, for the mosquitoes were moving. Although wet as a Labrador, I was quite warm. I have always felt flattered at being kicked around by a river as decent as this one. You have no idea how often I have been flattered!

When my clothes were half dry and thoroughly smoked, I put them on and went at it again. The magic hour was at hand. On the high bank of the Brule it was still full daylight, but down in the trough was the beginning of darkness. That is the time! That is the time when big old trout, thick through the shoulders, come cautiously out from beneath banks and brush tangles, and a man looks carefully to that part of his tackle extending from the line-leader knot to the knot that links fly to gut.

In this place the evening feeders will invariably be browns. I nailed one of a good pound and a half from a spot where I have taken a dozen like him. He was a push-over. I knew him as I knew his relatives, which I had eaten. He was ready to feed. It was darkening. Anything reasonably like trout feed would satisfy him. The Jock Scott, No. 6, was good enough. He took it and dived for his cave down under that bank. I horsed him out into midstream, where he was at a disadvantage, and then, by virtue of the stout leader rather than any boasted skill, I ran him ragged. I think he was finally glad to flop into my net. Anyway, I was glad!

There was another one, ten minutes later, which deceived me badly. He was of about the same vintage, a good Brule brown, called "lunker" in some waters. He too came forth willingly to battle and took the beaten Jock Scott so quickly that he was back under the snags and tying me up on a root before I knew what was happening.

Never mind. Losing one Jock Scott is part of an evening on the Brule. I have lost many more than one. I have come away from there so sorely beaten that I have seriously considered giving it all up. That I would be back the next night after work is, of course, understood by all men who love fly rods.

One night on this particular stretch of the Brule, with George Babb, the greatest trout-getter who ever arched a fly in my bailiwick, I had hold of a brown that swam into my vision like a muskalonge ... But this is just getting on into a fisherman's conversation, which is a one-sided affair, with a fellow hanging on to another fellow's coat lapel and talking his head off.

There was not much time left. But there was still time to look down a straight, flat stretch of the Brule and see the final light of the sun make the water gray. There was still time to make out a snagged fly in a spruce, climb the tree and save the fly, for it was one of my scarce-as hen's-teeth Jock Scotts.

Fly Fishing With MacQuarrie

And there was still time to mark the yearling doe as she froze — a statue on the bank at my right, befuddled, I think, by my immobility and the smell of citronella and oil of pennyroyal which drifted down to her. She held her ground even when I snorted, a trick for stopping deer which is done with the tongue against the roof of the mouth.

I worked down through the flat stretch, and at the end of it I found Mister President. I had expected to catch him a bit upstream. He was stretched out on top of the bank by the stone dam. The wind hits in there; so the mosquitoes had not scourged him. He was on his back, asleep, his rod at his side and his creel a few feet away.

I looked inside the creel. There wasn't a sign of a fish in it. From nearby came the regular rhythm of Mister President's snoring. The river, up and down stream, was a misty ribbon, losing itself in the night. And then, as I tip-toed so as not to waken him, there came from somewhere down around Rainbow Bend the song of eternal sweetness as a sleepy white-throat gave his final benediction to the day.

"*Trout waters can be very personal places. The best trout streams are the ones you grow up with and then grow old with. Eventually, they become like a familiar shotgun, or a faithful old setter, or a comfortable pair of shoes. You develop a profound affection for them and you think maybe before you die you will even understand a little about them.*"

Be forewarned. MacQuarrie has many snares to envelope you. The first is a lyric, Celtic quality. The Celts, says my textbook, "worshipped the loveliness of nature, loved life, loved love." The unforgettable lines from Romeo and Juliet are Celtic. How they bubbled out of a red-headed newspaperman's typewriter is anyone's guess. And notice the way MacQuarrie slides them in! Just when he's rollicking along tangled up in a fish line or fallen flat on his face in the river, whoops! here come the graceful singing sentences that make you pause and ponder and be warmed.

Now, In June

No time is better for trout fishermen than early June. Other months may approach it. They may even excel it now and then. But what I am getting at is that June is the best time for trout fishermen, as well as trout fishing.

Take the President of the Old Duck Hunters' Association, Inc., for instance. This symbolic angler said to me one night in knee-deep June in his back yard, "I can tell by the smell in the air I am going trout fishing tomorrow."

It was a good smell. Flowers were coming up out of brown earth. Insects hummed. The neighborhood was suffused with the odors of lush June. You smelled it and, smelling it, wondered if you would take those stuffy waders tomorrow or just an old pair of pants for wading.

"Yes, sir," said Mr. President, "I can smell trout tonight. I can smell 'em along towards tomorrow night on the Namakagon below Cable. I will just put me in there at Squaw Bend for maybe not more 'n an hour or two. It'll be dusk when the wind dies; so the mosquitoes will help me change flies.

First, I will eat supper in the car. I will be pretty lazy about it. I will not be hurried, you understand? I will set there a spell. I'll bet I hardly move a muscle until I hear the first whippoorwill. Then after a bit I will jump in below the county trunk bridge and tempt providence and the good brown trout of the Namakagon with large, unscientific, come-sundown flies. That is what I will do."

Imagine a man in this feverish age, twenty-four hours beforehand, declaring exactly what he will do twenty-four hours hence, come what will as to weather, business or the current status of his sciatic rheumatism.

"Yep," he reiterated there in his back yard, "I will drive down past McKinney's drug-store there in Cable and over to the river, and just as I'm arriving at Squaw Bend four cars with Illinois license plates will be pulling out. These will be city fishermen who don't know any better than to fish for Namakagon browns in broad daylight. They will be sore at the river. They will tell me there ain't a brown in the river — never was! They will go away from there, leaving it to me just when I want it, as the fishing gets good.

"I'm danged if I can figger out what trout fishermen these days are thinking about. They start at 10 A.M., after a good night's rest and a leisurely breakfast. They fish until the six o'clock whistle, and wonder why they don't get 'em. People like that are not entitled to catch trout. To catch trout, you got to suffer and learn."

He carried out the next day's schedule to a T. He abandoned his business at three, and one hour later came up my front walk in khaki trousers, his eyes snapping. I was only half ready. There had been a slight argument at our house. My wife, who is Mister President's daughter, just sort of hung around and looked abused while I picked up my stuff. That can unnerve people like me.

The President took in matters at a glance and yelped: "For heaven's sake, woman! Get away from that man! Can't you see he ain't soaked his leaders yet?"

Think of it! A man who can talk like that and make it stick! Picking up the final odds and ends, however, I wondered for the hundredth time why he could not command so imperiously in his own house, where he achieves his ends by other means — obsequiousness, if not downright chicanery. It's a smart man who knows when he's licked.

"Trout fishing is not like drinking beer," he lectured as the car sped south and east. "It's more like sipping champagne. A good beer drinker just sits him down and lays into it. You hear the first one splash. But you just sip champagne. You take a tiny leetle bit and smack your lips.

"So with trout. You don't want too many. You want to get the stage all set. You look ahead and figger out every move. You will not be rushed. You are not after a pail of fish. If you are, you would go down to the St. Croix and jerk the derned teeth out of smallmouths. What you are after is to fool a trout, or maybe four or five.

"I'm for filling frying pans, you understand. But only now and then. More often I'm for picking out a trout so smart he thinks of running for the legislature. There he is, living under the bank by daylight and sneering at the guys, who waste their time working over him when the sun is high. My idea of perfection is to give that guy a dose of sprouts — to teach him a lesson he won't forget, if I can't creel him."

"Then you have some places in mind ..."

"I'll thank you not to poke into other people's affairs and also to stay away from that hole two hundred yards below the town road, where the big dead stump sticks out into the river."

"Agreed. In return, will you avoid the fast rip below the island?"

"Why should I fool with half-pounders?" he snorted. "Your ten-cent rips are secure against trespass."

We drove under Cable's gorgeous pines, past McKinney's drug-store, which has seen more big browns than most drug stores, past the sawmill, and thence to the Namakagon at Squaw Bend, which is some place.

"Not exactly slightly known, however," Mister President replied when I raised the question. "Too dog-gone well known. But, happily, not intimately to fishermen who will play its own game."

"Like who?"

Now, In June

"Like me. Me, I wouldn't come down here a-whipping and a-lashing this crick in broad daylight. Oh, mebbe I would on an overcast, windy day. And how many of those do we get in a season? Me, I'd come down here either first thing in the morning or last thing at night. I'd rather do this than mow the lawn, I would ..."

He wheeled the car across a shallow, dry ditch, and it settled on low, hard ground, off the road. Twenty feet away the Namakagon journeyed by in the last direct rays of the sun. He broke out sandwiches and coffee and forbade me to move out of the car "until the time is ripe."

There was the dear old river. And sure enough, two disgusted fishermen coming to their car, parked nearby, who answered a hail with "You can have our share of it."

"Imagine!" snorted the President. "The exalted conceit of people who will fish this creek on a day the sky is so bright it isn't blue, but white! There they go, and fair weather after them. Quitting at seven o'clock. You know, I think this present generation of trout fishermen is afraid of the dark!"

Softly comes the night along the Namakagon. Born in cold, crooked-shored Namakagon Lake, it curves south and west to the St. Croix, its upper reaches trout water, its lower reaches smallmouth water almost on a par with the St. Croix itself.

There it was, just beyond the car windows, gray and ropy in the growing dusk. It ran under the county trunk bridge,

surged to the right and lost itself around the corner, where
there is a grand series of rips. You just look at that kind of
river in June and want to plump right into it.

Not, however, when the President is in charge. We sat
and munched. In that far northern corner of Wisconsin,
darkness comes slowly in early June. That is a great help to
deliberate evening campaigners. Those twilights were made
for trout fishermen. They give you time, the President says,
"to square off at it."

It was a night to remember, and the Old Duck Hunters
remember many such and are properly thankful. June along
the Namakagon is a month of heavy perfumes and many
birds. No stretch of the Namakagon in the Cable-Seeley
country offers more than the Squaw Bend territory.

Trout waters can be very personal places. The best trout
streams are the ones you grow up with and then grow old
with. Eventually they become like a familiar shotgun, or a
faithful old setter, or a comfortable pair of shoes. You develop a profound affection for them, and you think maybe
before you die you will even understand a little about them.

We went downstream, he on the right bank, I on the left.
At this putting-in place, high above the right bank, stretches the level top of an old logging railroad grade. The light
was waning in the west, and the top of this embankment cut
off the sky like a knife. Below this ran the churning river, far
noisier and more mysterious than it had been an hour
before.

Now, In June

Certainly you must know how it is to come to a place like this. A place you know well. A place where you are on intimate terms with the smallest boulders, where yonder projecting limb once robbed you of a choice fly, where from beneath the undercut banks the big ones prowl by night to claim the larger morsels of the darkness.

Strange and utterly irresistible are such places to trout fishermen. There you had hold of a good one. Here you netted a smaller one. Down beyond the turn in the pool below the old snag pile you lost still another. The spell of approaching night silenced the President, but not for long.

"One thing I can't figger out," he said finally. His voice came to me from a point downstream, drifting over the purring waters in the sweet June air, "How can a Scotch Presbyterian like you enjoy anything that's so much fun?"

He vanished in the gloom like some wise and ancient spirit of the river. I heard his wader brogues nick a rock as he stumbled, heard him cuss softly and then the river took me in ...

Though it is early June, the mosquitoes are not bad. One of those rare nights when the pesky hordes fail to discover you there in mid-river. The temperature had dropped quickly from a sunlit 80 or so to below 70, and you know it will be a night for blankets. You know, too, as the water laps at waders that it is the cool, kindly hand of night which chills your river every twenty-four hours and makes it livable for trout.

Fly Fishing With MacQuarrie

You are as relaxed, physically and mentally, as you will ever be. The river has reached out like an old friend and made a place for you. You pack a leisurely pipe, and the water about you is lit for a minute, the match hisses in the river and the babbling mystery of the night deepens.

The current plucks at your knees. Your fingers feel in the darkness for the familiar shapes of bass-sized trout flies. A whim will decide which one. From long experience you have learned to hold fingers toward the western sky as you bend on your choice.

What to do? Work the right bank down, foot by foot, with the short, efficient line of the after-sunset angler? Or cover all the water methodically, persistently?

Plop! A Namakagon brown has decided the issue for you. He is downstream maybe as much as fifty yards, and a good fat plop it is. Just the kind of trout you would expect to come prowling out from the snags on a cool June evening. You know it is the careless fling of a worthy brown, and you are pretty sure he will look at something big and buggy, that he is confident and bellicose.

But just a minute now! You've tried these fish before in the near dark. They come quickly and they go quickly. Once pricked, they standeth not upon the ceremony of their departing. You tighten up a bit. Browns, though more fool-hardy by night, can still be very chancy. You do, however, reach around and feel for the net handle, but quickly make personal amends to whatever fishing gods there be. You know it does not pay to be cocky. You know you must study to be humble and alert.

You take it easy in getting to a spot upstream from the fish. You get over to the left bank for your little stalk, and you lift your feet high and put them down easily. You study the vague outline of the branches with which you will have to contend in casting. You take long, hard drags at the little blackened pipe, so that the bowl glows hot. You are on edge and ready. You get within thirty-five feet of the place and wait ...

Plop! Good! He is not frightened. You false-cast with the big fly, wondering how to show it to him. A slack-line drift down over him? Or cross-current cast and a smart retrieve? You decide on the former. It will disturb the water less, and you can come back to the fussier cast later.

You lengthen line, and you know your fly is going over his window. Nothing. Again and again you cast, letting it drift below him and out into midstream. And you retrieve each time carefully, so as not to whip his top water and frighten him. Still nothing. He isn't seeing it.

Very well. You have covered all corners of his window with the dead floating fly. You have shown him Business No. 1, and he wants none of it. Very well. Now for action, a la bass stream. Zip-zip-zip! The fly is brought back over his window in short jerks.

Ka-doong! That was the medicine. He's got it. He's fast and he's heavy and he's going places.

Fly Fishing With MacQuarrie

Now, for Pete's sake, take it easy. The leader is sound and the stream is free of stuff, except for that undercut bank. He is bucking like a mule. You strip in a couple of feet; tentatively, and exult at your strategy in showing him an actionable fly, something struggling and toothsome.

He's certainly husky. Those Namakagon busters are built like tugboats. He's sidewise now, below you, in midstream, giving you the works. He has broken water a couple times. He rushes you and you strip in like mad, letting the retrieved line fall where it may in the current.

And then after you have given him Mister President's "dose of sprouts," and you reach around and feel the hickory handle of the net ...

Like many another after-dark brown on the Namakagon, this one was a good pound and a half. I did not see him until he was in the net, and that is unusual. Generally you see living flashes of fleshy brown out there in the gloom. He was reddish and thick and cold as ice as I removed the fly, tapped him on the head and slid him into the wide, deep jacket pocket I use for a creel.

I was trembling. I can't take 'em without quaking. They get right down under me, and turn flip-flops inside. The pipe was out. The stripped line was bellied downstream. The fly was chewed. It was a pattern evolved by a friend whose stamping ground is the surging river Wolf. A few of its devotees gave it a name a year back — Harvey Alft's Nonpareil — and it has stuck.

Now, In June

I went over and sat on a boulder near the bank. Just one trout — and all that fuss. I sat and wondered, as all men have, if the day would ever come when I could take so small a fraction of a trout stream's population and not develop a galloping pulse.

I have caught more trout than I deserve to catch. And always and forever, the good ones like this fellow put me on edge, send me hippity-hopping to a boulder or the bank to sit down and gather my wits.

Another pipeful helped settle things. I thought, sitting there, another bold trout might betray himself by leaping, but none did. I tested the leader, smoked out the pipe and went back upstream by the left bank. Now the first plan of campaign would be in order — fish the right bank like a machine. Swish-swish. That was the only sound there in the dark as the Nonpareil sailed back and out, back and out. Maybe there would be one or two right in close to the bank, just outside the protecting roots.

There was. Indeed there was. Another golden-bellied Namakagon brown mouthed Harvey Alft's Nonpareil with sure determination and made for midstream and faster water. He was smaller, but lively. I horsed him a bit. You are permitted to do that when you are building up to a brace. A pair is so much better than a loner. Two more were netted through the methodical casting toward the right bank, out from which they lay feeding. And there is little excuse for repeating the old, old story.

101

Fly Fishing With MacQuarrie

It was getting on toward 10 P.M., which is the time you quit on trout streams in Wisconsin. I moved downstream to the sacred precincts of Mister President's pool. The whip-poorwills were in a dither. A deer splashed at the stream bank and snorted back through the brush. The flat top of the old logging grade was now lit by the stars.

I was proud of my four fish. I showed them to him. He said they were fish that would disgrace no man's skillet. He was sitting on the bank in the dark. His glowing cigar end attracted me. He was a little weary, and I felt a little guilty when he pounded me on the back and then said he had nothing — "but I had hold of one — the one!"

Nothing for Mister President. I do not like to wind up trout trips with him that way. And, in all conscience, I seldom do!

We followed the bank back to the car and pulled off our waders. It was just ten o'clock. He slumped a little over the wheel, for he was beaten and he was tired. And then, before he stepped on the starter, he rolled down a window and took a good, long sniff of the Namakagon's June aroma.

"You know," he said, "I can tell by the smell in the air I am going trout fishing tomorrow."

Thus we come, belatedly, to another MacQuarrie lesson. He unabashedly preferred old things to new things. The old alarm clock that ran only when face down. Hundred-year-old decoys that were "game to the core." Here, them old time flies. Tested. Proven. Known values. No guessing about these beauties.

Things were marching along when this yarn appeared in 1947. He mentions the development of nymphs, bivisibles and fanwings. But the days of blazing Hi-Tech that mark our era lie far distant. Would MacQuarrie have approved? Sure. His job required he keep current with "Progress." But down deep in the man — as with Mr. President, indeed, perhaps in all of us — he preferred them old time flies. (I'll let you find for yourself what he caught his fish on.)

Them Old
Time Flies

The Brule River of Wisconsin lay fifteen miles out of my way, but I drove to it anyway, like a swain to his true love. The look of it disappointed me. Standing on the Winnebojou wagon ridge, I felt that the river was off form.

I can hardly explain why I felt that way. Perhaps it was the absence of rising trout, or the recollection of the prolonged hot spell which, even as I stood there studying the current, sent sweat down my neck. Or it might have been the long summer water plants streaming from the Brule's bottom in places.

I'm making a mess out of trying to explain something I cannot rightly explain. To make certain of my hunch, I diverged farther from my route and inspected the river from other points, including Stone's bridge, which spans the upper river a good forty-five miles from Lake Superior, as the river goes.

This place seldom fails to quicken my pulse, which is the

way things are between the Brule and me. There have been times at this old putting-in place when, in a canoe with trout rising, I have missed a guide or two in my rod while stringing up. This particular evening it left me cold. Maybe it didn't look right because I couldn't remain and fish it, even if I had wanted to. There was work to do in other places. Who can say how much of a fisherman's judgment depends upon his own state of mind? And how much of his success?

It was late in August the next time I braked down the Winnebojou hill and leaned over the steel bridge rail to look again upon this lovely river. So help me, it looked right! Actually, it seemed no different. The same cold, ropy water came around the bend and whispered under the bridge. The same whippoorwills were making the same old music. The same absence of rising trout was noted. But it looked right.

Gentlemen, you may hang, draw and quarter me, but I can contribute no more to the angler's relentless pursuit of cause and effect than to say the stream looked right. I have seen other fishermen in such throes — certain they would be successful, but not able to explain their confidence. I remember an evening on the Brule at quitting time years ago. Carl Miller, a guide, was standing on Stone's bridge gloomily studying the water. It was the end of a poor day of fishing. "She won't be worth a darn for three days," he said. "Come back then." He didn't know why. It turned out subsequently that he was correct.

Them Old Time Flies

So, with a feeling that the augur was good, I drove along — up Johnny Degerman's hill toward the vast, sand pine barrens which feed their rainfall to the Brule, and came eventually to a low-lying log cabin where a light gleamed. There, beneath the light, the President of the Old Duck Hunters' Association, Inc., sat reading a two-week-old newspaper.

"Thought you'd drop by on the way north," he greeted. "Where you been?"

"Never mind, sir. Have you caught any trout?"

"The Brule hasn't been right."

It turned out that he had "a hatful of trout" taken from a creek of minor distinction called Long Branch. They tasted so good that I washed and wiped the dishes. We sat, talking.

"She looked right when I passed by," I said.

"Been pretty warm."

"Nights are cooler and longer," I pressed.

"If you've got a full day, we could slip down to the Chippewa Flowage and show our collection of big hardware to the muskies."

"How cool was it when you got up this morning?"

"Forty-one at 6 A.M."

"Been cool right along — nights?"

"Two blankets."

"We'll fish the Brule, your Honor!"

The Old Man tamped new tobacco over old in his

crooked pipe. "We could get us some bass. Drift from the iron bridge on the Namakagon down to the St. Croix. Get Jens to pick up out at nine."

"She looked right to me, I tell you."

"Oh, the Brule. Hm-m-m. How about us getting a half dozen big suckers and lacing the flowage for one big muskie?"

"Mister President." I said, rather sharply, considering my junior membership in the Association, "why don't you want to fish the Bois Brule when I say she looks right, and when there are only ten days left of the season?"

He came clean: "Dang it to blazes! I lost my fly-book on Long Branch, that derned, ornery, deep-valleyed, wood-tick-ridden drainage ditch!"

This was serious. Mister President's fly-book was a fly-book! It was three inches thick, loaded with trout flies which had become for him precious talismen in thirty-five years of filling it with flies. A thing with a tattered leather cover, worn but efficient. It hurt to know it was gone.

"I have with me at least four hundred flies," I offered.

"Not my kind of flies."

I had him cold there. I went to my car and produced an aluminum box in which were stored only flies which he had given me over a period of twenty years. I spilled them out on the table, explaining where I had got them. His eyes brightened as he saw beneath the table lamp the dull maroon of ancient ragged Montreals, the brazen red of

108

Parmacheene Belles, the silvery blue of Silver Doctors.

In that noble old collection, some of which had seen thirty years of service, were wet flies in the great old tradition — bright McGintys, plain and Royal Coachmen, Cowdungs, Seth Greens, Grizzly Kings, Brown Hackles, Black Gnats — all the common, proven wet flies which Mister President had learned to trust through performance. It seemed to me then that he might rejoice. Instead he chose to drive a point, the while scooping up the antiques and restoring them to their compartments.

Fly Fishing With MacQuarrie

"Right there's all the flies a man needs. What's come over this new generation of fishermen? They've got to have something new every whipstitch. I know people tying flies who never went fishing in their lives. Yes, sir! They take it up like women take up needlework — and make flies for hatbands, not for fishing. Imagine!

"And what sort of flies?" He rose to magnificent oratory. "The gol-dangedst, no-name, hybrid, sloppy-hackled flies imaginable. You know what" — shaking a finger under my nose — "there was a time when a hundred patterns of flies were known and proven. Today there are ten thousand!"

"You don't have to use them, your honor."

"And I ain't gonna!"

He fingered the box, sort of caressing it, and I thought again he would mellow, but he continued: "I've got no quarrel with new fangled flies if they deliver the goods. What I object to are non-fishing amateurs twisting up flies like so many idiots because they like the colors." He fairly snorted. "Why, lots of them are using neck hackle from old brokendown hens that should have been pensioned instead of plucked!"

I reminded him that there had been some splendid developments in fly rod lures these last twenty-five years — nymphs, bivisibles, new streamers, spiders, fanwings. He agreed grudgingly, patted the box of old flies, wound his six-ounce gold watch deliberately and went to bed, calling: "Set the alarm for 2:30. We've got twenty miles to drive."

Them Old Time Flies

It was certainly a chilly morning, such a one as the north can turn up in late August to make a man think of hunting to come. In the night I had dragged two blankets over me. The alarm petered out, and its dying sound was joined, then replaced by the clank of the kitchen pump. As usual, Mister President had beat the clock. He was in his waders and brogues. "Might as well put 'em on. It's a cold morning, and we'll save time when we get there by wearing 'em."

Mister President nursed his heavy old car deliberately and carefully down the narrow trail between the pine trees. The pre-dawn deer were abroad, standing in the glare of the lamps so that twice Mister President had to apply the brakes. Snowshoe rabbits darted across the road. At one inroad where we stopped to reconnoiter Mister President swished a bush with his foot and heavy dew flashed.

"Two degrees lower, and we'd have had a frost," he remarked.

The place where we stopped, after some debate, was not the spot twenty miles distant to which we first planned going. This place was thirty miles away from our starting point, attained by a road to the lower Brule, over hogback clay hills, not more than a few miles from Lake Superior. Hizzoner turned the car into a small meadow, and by the car lights we saw that frost had barely brushed the grass tops.

"Bet those waders feel good now," said Mister President. "Frosts every month of the year down here." He had insist-ed on this lower reach of river "because there'll be some early browns from the lake working in. Might even hook a rainbow, though it's early for that."

The Brule and many other Midwestern streams produce rainbow runs at the end of summer. Little is known about these runs. The big runs of rainbows are in the spring.

Before he departed downstream he held the box of ancient flies to the brightening eastern sky, with the cover open, as though to assure himself that these were the same friends of his younger days. Ordinarily at this place I go upstream from a wooden bridge. I like upstream fishing, wet or dry, on the Brule or any place.

This morning, with Mister President's warning of possible browns in from Lake Superior, I went downstream, but not with the Old Man. It never does for a fisherman of this Association to follow another one, stepping on his heels. Anyway, not at the beginning of the day. Later, when sociability becomes more important than trout, the members of this Association customarily make a rendezvous and fish together. Mister President is a downstream man by habit, a product of the wet-fly days.

I walked up two of the clay hogbacks and struck north, through brush, to get below Mister President. The going was bad — heavy spruce in low places, endless popple and hazel on higher lands. After the battle with the brush, it was a relief to slip into the Brule at a wide spot and sort of lean back against the current. It had been so cold in the night that the mosquitoes were dormant. Ramparts of spruce leaned on the right bank, with here and there a solitary cork pine.

Within five minutes Mister President's hunch about Gitche Gumee browns came true. One grabbed my wet squirrel-tail streamer, darted sidewise in heavy current and snapped the 3x leader as easily as that. I put on a heavier leader with the same pattern of streamer, and the second one did not get away. He went about a pound and a half and felt very good as he shaped to the 16-inch width of my fish pocket. This, I decided, was going to be easy.

A half hour later, with nothing more in the fish pocket, I reminded myself what the Old Man would have said, had he been there: "Pride goeth before fall, and right after fall you get a long, hard winter."

I tried spinners and combinations with flies. I turned around and faced the current, floating flies and dunking them. The sun got above the horizon and lit up the tops of the spruces. A few of the hardier mosquitoes punched the clock and manned their drills. A little wind came blowing against the northwest. Partridge drummed. The Brule mocked me.

In desperation I turned downstream again, biting off gut and replacing flies until I remembered what the Old Man had said one day: "Son you're gonna wear down your front teeth on silk-worm gut," and then he calmly bit through his own heavy leader and changed his fly.

The Brule has often whipped me — much more often

than it has suddenly turned into a place I felt was the world with a fence around it and full of trout. This odd river does this to me at just about the time I begin to think golf is a pretty good game after all, considering the shower-bath that goes with it.

The fly that did it was a soft-hackled monstrosity on a long-shank hook. No name for it. Just something somebody tied up. Like most trout fishermen, I have traded flies with the brethren from coast to coast. It's a good custom, indicative of the fraternity that prevails among men who fish trout. The predominant colors of this nondescript were purple, and yellow, and the minute it hit the surface its soft hackle subsided so that, drawn through the water, it was just a streak of color.

You have seen flies like this, often tied by local amateurs, in hatbands, clipped to cardboard sales displays, and perhaps speared through the corner of a letter to you from some hopeful who writes: "Give it a try and let me know" The hook on which it was tied was thin, but it wasn't brittle. It bent some on the second solidly hooked brown, and it bent on the third and fourth and the fifth, so that each time I'd have to straighten it a little. And each time I straightened it and looked at its complete lack of distinction I had to say: "I'll be damned!"

I don't know why they went for that funny fly any more than I know why the Brule looked good to me the evening before. Every fish it took was a brown; one went close to two pounds. They felt good as I went back upstream through the streamside brush, sweating. It would be another hot day. None but those who had been there at 3:30 A.M. could believe that frost had kissed the lower Brule bottoms a few hours before.

In the mile and a half of water I passed going back I did not find Mister President, or anyone else. I got all the way back to the car in the meadow and looked across the current. The car doors were closed. No rod leaned against it. Where was Mister President? I was about to wade the river when he emerged from the spruce at the edge of the meadow.

Carrying a World War I trench shovel under his arm, he peered into and poked at a red tobacco tin as he walked. He stowed the shovel in the car trunk, hitched up his patched waders, took his rod from where it leaned against a lone spruce at the river's edge and glided along the Brule's right bank, downstream. I knew exactly where he was going, to a place called McNeil's Pool.

With angleworms! Ah, the old flies, the good old proven killers. Can You blame me for laughing out loud as I waded the Brule to the car? Can you blame me for chuckling as I got out of my waders? As the Old Man came striding out of the spruce with the shovel and the worm can he looked exactly like a fellow who has said to himself: "Well, boys, here is where all friendship ceases. I am now going to put on a pair of brass knuckles and take the joint apart!"

Fly Fishing With MacQuarrie

I put my gear away and let down the car windows. The wind was strong enough to discourage the deer flies, so I dozed. It was near noon when the car door opened and Mister President yelled, "Roll out, you whelp of a boy, and have a look at some old-time trout caught with old-time flies!"

He laid before me on the grass a creelful of magnificent browns, topped by one three-pound rainbow, a pale hard-fleshed thing which might have been a steelhead, but we won't go into that here.

He was simply jubilant. "Reminds me of the old days," he said, "when Fred and I used to take our limits of brooks in an hour — on those old time flies, son. You can't beat 'em."

I showed him my fish He felt so good about everything that he did not even sneer at them. He said, "Mighty nice pan-fish there, son, mighty nice."

On the way back to the shack he got off about four moralistic sermons on the virtues of old-time flies, in such language as would have done credit to Chautauqua's greatest spellbinders, including Bill Bryan. He was tired; so I toted the gear from the car down the hill to the place. While he stretched out on a couch I scrubbed the new potatoes, made the salad, brewed the tea and did up four trout in deep fat.

All through the meal he regaled me with the morning's events: "You take that dark Montreal and let 'er sink, retrieving with slow jerks — nothing better ... As for a Silver Doctor, I like it out in midstream, where the water's fast ... Might be they think it's a minnie ..."

While I washed the dishes he kept it up. I heard the history of the old time flies told and retold. "You take that Tom Bosworth, tied the plain Coachman. Used to drive for Queen Victoria. Could flick a pipe out of the mouth of a man with his whip as he drove the old lady around London ... Must have been a piece of a man."

He fell asleep on the couch, and I straightened up our gear. As I picked up his fishing jacket from the heap on the floor, the red tin tobacco can fell from a pocket. It was empty. Bits of fresh dried earth clung to it. I set it on the mantelpiece and finished straightening things up. Then I placed the empty tin on a card table, beside the Old Man's couch, with a sign penciled on cardboard: "Them Old-Time Flies."

He awoke around four in the afternoon, yawned, stretched, looked at his watch, saw the display and chuckled.

"You can't beat 'em! How 'bout you and me getting in a little bass fishing 'fore dark?"

We must now examine humor. At any time it is a rare commodity. And it's tough on editors. They read a story and find it funny. Then they reread it and it isn't so funny. After the third or fourth reading (editors read at lightning speed or they don't stay editors long), all the humor has vanished and the author often gets the piece back.

MacQuarrie is one of four men of his day who are still in print and read. Havilah Babcock had a quiet sense of humor. Archibald Rutledge took a backseat to none where poetic expression was concerned, but his adventures with Prince, wonderful as they are, can't be called humorous. Nash Buckingham is pretty much straight forward with a smile now and then thrown in. But MacQuarrie's bubbly sense of fun is unique. He never works at being funny, give or take a pratfall or two. His humor is just there. In MacQuarrie himself. In Mr. President. They view life as a game, a grand game, at which you either have to laugh or cry.

These guys, thank heaven, choose to laugh. And we laugh with them.

The Kitchen-Sink Fish

In the month of May, when spring is a blessed fact in most places, churlish Lake Superior declines to be a good neighbor. This greatest of fresh-water bodies hangs on to departing winter by its coat-tails, fights hard to keep its vast ice-fields from withering before the prairie winds. Some days the westerly winds drive the ice-floes beyond sight of land. Then the wind shifts, and back come the chalk-white rafts to jam the bays and harbors and river mouths. When the lake wind is king, its cold will be felt some distance inland.

A strange climate, this. Raw winter in control on the lake shore many a day when, fifteen miles inland, the country is soaking up 70- and 80-degree warmth. At least one newspaper in a lake-shore city has acknowledged this whimsical weather by publishing, daily in spring, the temperature not only of the city but of the interior at a point thirty miles away. Thus lake dwellers learn when they may escape the cold wind in a game of golf, a country ride — or a bit of fishing.

Now, coursing down for sixty-six miles to the south shore of this chilly old lake is the river Brule. Early in the season this estimable trout stream may, in its upper reaches, soak in 90 degrees, while down below, near the lake, the Brule runs through temperatures of 45 or so degrees.

Strange things can happen to a fisherman in Maytime along this storied Wisconsin stream. A man can fish it of a morning near the lake and see ice form in his rod guides. Later, hunting the sun, he can drive to an upper river put-in and get his neck thoroughly sunburned, and wish to high heaven he had left off the long underwear.

You who fish it — and every troutster hopes he will — should be forewarned so that you may come with clothing appropriate both for late winter and full summer. The only solution is two kinds of apparel. Many's the time I have hit the lower Brule dressed like an Eskimo, and then gone upstream and cooled my feet by dangling them over the side of a canoe.

A good many of the faithful, like the President of the Old Duck Hunters' Association, Inc., are firm believers in celebrating the opening along the more arctic portions of the Brule. There is sound reason for this. At the average opening many of the big, migratory rainbows from Lake Superior have finished spawning and are working back to the home waters.

The Kitchen-Sink Fish

"A man would be a ninnyhammer," said Mister President to me, "to pass up that first crack at the big ones."

"Habit is a powerful thing," said I.

Well did he know my affection for the upper reaches and its chance for trout, albeit smaller ones, on smaller lures: namely and to wit, dry floating flies, than which no finer device to deceive fish has been conceived in the mind of man.

Anyway, we went fishing on the lower river, come opening day. It was a morning to gladden pneumonia specialists. Emerging from the warm car at the streamside, I was as eager to embrace the flood as I am to get up in a deer camp and light the fire. Braver men than I have quailed at such fishing. I can remember huge Carl Tarsrud, stellar Brule fisherman, six feet four of Viking stamina, declaring in John Ziegler's gun repair shop that he wouldn't have any part of that lower Brule on an ugly first day.

Well, there we were, us Old Duck Hunters, as far asunder in fraternal spirit as ever we were. It made me shiver just to look at that part of the Brule. We were down below Armstead's farm, north of the town of Brule. There were snowy patches in the hollows, the day was gray, and from the lake blew a searching cold.

The Rt. Hon. President was lively as a cricket. His brown eyes snapped. He had buckled into waders while I was pulling on extra socks — reluctantly. For him the birds were singing and the sun was shining. In him the flame of the

121

zealot burns with a fierce light. He went to the river whistling. I followed in a dampened frame of mind.

Against the rigors of the day I had seen to it that there was a full quart thermos of scalding coffee in my jacket. I knew, too, that the President was similarly fortified, from the bulge in his own jacket. As I waded out into the rocky stream it came to me that, if worst came to worst, it was always possible to go ashore, light a fire, and drown my woes guzzling coffee.

Hizzoner had no thought of coffee at the moment. He hastened away down the little path on the left bank and embraced the current a hundred yards below me. This was duck soup for him. You knew, watching even at that distance, no shiver passed through his wiry frame, and you thought, disgusted, what frightful fanaticism possesses a man who thus cleaves to his private poison under any conditions.

I remember how cold I got. I remember how my hands got blue, how I dreaded changing flies or plucking with numb fingers for lethargic angleworms in the bait can. I remember how the river cold bit through waders and wool and drove me, time and again, to perching on stream rocks. I remember how I thought wader pockets would be handy things to have, and how I pressed hands into armpits to restore warmth.

But, best of all, I remember the big splash I made when worn hobnails betrayed me and I bounced, more horizontal than vertical, off a flat rock into four feet of water. Then the river claimed me completely, so that my under wools and my outer wools were soaked and only a wild grab saved my hat from drifting away.

Ah — the coffee! And the warming fire! A big one. And may the devil fly away with every rainbow trout in the lower Brule, for all of me. They weren't hitting anyway. Blessed coffee. Blessed fire.

Now for a match. Whazzat, no match-safe? Had I left it home this evil day, after toting it for years and years? I had, verily. Oh, foolish man. Oh, bitter cold. Well, the coffee, then. And quick, Henri, for there's a man freezing to death! Ah — a whole quart, scalding hot!

I unscrewed the aluminum top and gazed into a container in which the fragile glass shell had broken into a million pieces. Those old, smooth hobs on my wading brogues had not only half drowned me, but had delivered the thermos to mine enemy, the rock.

A pretty pickle In ten minutes I'd be ready for an oxygen tent. I have fallen into many a river and many a lake. Annually I achieve swan dives, jack-knifes, half-gainers and standing-sitting-standing performances. I am an expert faller-in. Poling a canoe up Big Falls on the Brule, I can, any day you name, describe a neat parabola and come up dripping with only one shin skinned. On my better days I can weave back and forth in exaggerated slow motion until the waters finally claim me.

Fly Fishing With MacQuarrie

Be assured, gentlemen, you are listening to no raw beginner at the diving game. But that one down below Armstead's farm really won me the championship of the Brule that season. That one was an even more convincing demonstration than one of several years before, when I fell head first out of a duck boat and went home by the light of the moon, strictly naked, my underwear drying on an oar.

"For two bits," I said, thinking of Mister President, "I would go look him up and give him a taste of it himself." It was just then the trail bushes parted, and there he was, dry as a bone, grinning like a skunk eating bumblebees, the tail of a big rainbow projecting from his game pocket. He took me in at a glance.

"Fell in on purpose so I'd feel sorry for you and we'd go to the upper river, eh?"

So much for sympathy from this Spartan who, when he falls in, keeps right on a-going. Nevertheless he produced his hot coffee and dry matches. While the fire roared and I draped clothing on bushes, he told me about the fish. "Down by those old pilings. Salmon eggs. I went downstream with him forty yards. He was in the air half the time."

Then he noticed that his ghillie was, in fact, in the blue lipped stage. He took off his jacket, threw it around me and pushed me closer to the fire, throwing down birch bark for me to stand upon. It seemed to me there lurked in his eyes a twinkle of sympathy, but I can never make sure about that with him. It may be deviltry. He built a drying frame for the wet clothes, and when an hour had passed and I was back into them, half dry and very smoky, he relented completely. He went the whole hog.

"Well, come on. You'll never get completely dry down here. I've got my kitchen-sink fish anyway."

The President thus describes the whale which he must annually stretch out in the sink before calling in the neighbors.

So it was that we pulled out of the lower Brule valley and drove south. In the town of Brule he stopped the car and went into a store with his now empty thermos bottle.

"A man has got to have coffee to fish," he said.

It was only around noon, and this far up the Brule valley the sun was shining. South we went over familiar trails: the ranger's road past round-as-a-dime Hooligan Lake, the county trunk, past Winnebojou where three hundred cars were parked and thence to Stone's Bridge where Johnny Degerman presided. Up there it was 75 above. There was a strong, gusty wind beating downstream. It was summer, and a few minutes before we had been in winter.

Let it be said here that on opening day along the Brule people who like to be alone will do best to stay above Winnebojou. Along this portion of the creek, for some twenty miles, most of the banks are owned privately, and ingress to same is not to be had at every turn-in gate along the county roads that parallel the stream. But the problem can be solved by going to Stone's Bridge, the common jumping-off place for upper river explorers.

If it is feasible to divide any river into two parts, the division may be effected on the Brule by nominating the Winnebojou Bridge as the equator. And connoisseurs of the difference between fact and fancy should be told, right here and now, that people who really know the creek will always refer to this particular spot as the Winnebojou Wagon Bridge, and you can figure out yourself when the last wagon crossed any bridge anywhere.

Still that is its traditional name. Upstream from it lie several million dollars' worth of real estate and lodges, including the fabulous Pierce estate of 4,400 acres. Downstream from it are the precincts of Tom, Dick and Harry and, let it be added, the best places for getting the big rainbows in the early run.

It was so warm up there at Stone's Bridge that Johnny Degerman, Charon of these waters, had his shirt open all the way down the front.

"Mr. Degerman, I believe," said the President in his best manner.

"Go to hell, the both of you," said Mr. Degerman, who was being bothered some by mosquitoes.

"Mr. Degerman!" the President reprimanded.

"I saved a canoe," said Johnny. "Thought you might be along. Could have rented it for five bucks. And all I get from you birds is a buck."

The Kitchen-Sink Fish

"Mr. Degerman," said the President, "your philanthropy moves me to the extent of promising to pay one buck and a half for said canoe."

"Lucky if I get the buck," said Johnny, who is a charming fellow. "And say, if you're smart, you'll show them something wet and big and brown. Carl Miller has been knocking their ears off with a big home-made Ginger Quill."

"Enough!" cried Hizzoner. "First you insult me, and then you rub it in by telling me what to throw at 'em. Gimme a canoe pole. I mean give him one. My back ain't so strong today."

So it was that the old Duck Hunters went forth abroad upon the bosom of the Brule and Mr. Degerman called after us, "I may pick up some chubs for you off'n the bridge, in case you don't connect."

We were too far away for the President to do more than look back at Johnny with what must pass as a haughty stare.

It was certainly a day. There was that downstream breeze, which means warmth. There was the smell of a million cedar trees. There was a good canoe under us, and ten miles of red hot river before us, and hundreds and hundreds of cedar waxwings letting on they were glad to be alive.

You know how it is. The signs are right. You feel history is in the making. You take your time buttering up the line. You are painstaking about soaping the surplus grease off the leader. You lay on the anti-mosquito kalsomine. You light a leisurely pipe and don't give a rap what happens tomorrow or the day after.

His nibs exercised seniority rights by occupying the bow with a rod the first hour. It was not too eventful. Small trout could be had for the casting, willing wallopers, mostly rainbows and brookies, which fought with terrier impudence. The worthier foes were lurking under the banks and in the deep holes. The only memorable excitement in five miles was a dusky native of about 16 inches which came out from under a brush heap to take the President's wet Cowdung.

For long years those upper Brule brookies have intrigued the O.D.H.A., Inc. We do not credit them with too much sense. But accuse us not of sacrilege, for we love them dearly. We love them so much that we wish they had more — well, foresight. In a hitting mood they are fly-rushers, show-offs, and that is the trouble. More common caution and less eagerness to lick the world would save many of them useless flops in the bottom of a willow-walled hereafter.

"Did I ever tell you about the Olson boys?" said the President at lunch at May's Rips. "They were taking out pine on a forty near Foxboro, and it was a whale of a big forty, because they got about a million feet off it one winter.

"Anyway, one morning, the kid — I forget his name — woke up late in the camp and began dressing. He couldn't find his socks, which is what happens to anyone who wakes up late in a well-regulated logging camp. So he says, says he: "Some low-down, no-good miscreant without the decency of a weasel swiped my socks! Was it you, Pa?"

The Kitchen-Sink Fish

There was more. Of Jack Bradley's aniline-dyed pigeons which he sold to visiting trout fishermen on the Big Balsam in the old days as holy birds of India. Of the same Jack's famous kangaroo court, where fishermen were sentenced for ungraceful Iying. Of times along the storied Brule when lumberjacks took out brook trout by the bushel on red-flannel-baited hooks. And there were tales of Old Mountain, the Brule's mythical gargantua, a rainbow trout whose ascent of the stream raised the water two feet; of his sworn enemy, the Mule, another rainbow, almost as big. That sort of thing didn't catch many fish, but along the Brule you are likely to feel it doesn't make any difference, one way or another.

We sat there, with our backs against cool cedars, and watched the river hustle by. Sometimes a canoe drifted past and a lazy hand would be raised, or a lazier Chippewa would exert himself for a minute, poling up the not-too-formidable fast water of May's Rips. But mostly we just sat and studied foam-flecked water spill down the rips, arrow into a water spear-head at the bottom and carom off to the left. It was almost three o'clock when the President leaped up.

"I don't know why in time I go fishing with you," he declared. "The day is almost over, and I've got only one kitchen-sink fish."

"Gimme," said I, "another doughnut — and shut up, will you?"

But the spell was broken. Mister President was on his

feet and there was a river to fish. I took the stern paddle, for it was my turn, and the canoe slid down May's Rips, under the rustic bridge, past the Pierce hatchery outflow, through the wide-spread and down threatening Big Falls, which looks worse than it is, but is bad enough.

Big Falls is just a good fast rip of river, almost completely arched by graceful cedars. You see it from the upstream side as hardly more than an inviting dark tunnel in the cedar forest wall. You see a little lip of curling water; and then when you are right on top of it and your eyes are adjusted to its darker light, you see it as a downhill stretch of roaring water, and unless you are good at twisting canoes around right-angled corners you may have trouble at the end, where it goes off to the left.

Big Falls is just another rapid to a good Brule Chippewa boatman. But neither the President nor I qualify in that respect. We are fair, just fair. On good days, when we are not too tired, we can, with care, bring a canoe back up Big Falls, a stunt the Chippewas do with a passenger — usually sitting, tensed, in the bottom. Well, Big Falls has licked me more often than vice versa, but I am resigned to winning up to about the eighth round, after which I fall in, or out, and grab the bow of the canoe and tow it the rest of the way.

We got down easily, and in the slack water the President said: "Hold 'er! Hold 'er and give me my waders."

For once, I had thought, we were to hit the upper river without recourse to long halts while Mister President climbed in and out of waders. It was not to be so, however. He had his same old scheme in mind: to tie up the canoe and wade the fast water below the Big Falls. He is a man who holds that the best way to catch trout is to meet them on their own terms, afoot.

Below Big Falls the Brule is touch-and-go wading in many spots. It goes down and it twists. It shoots between banks of huge gray cedars, and in places the trees almost meet overhead. Its bottom is rock-strewn. Its current is swift. Here, you would say, is a hunk of river that would be at home in the mountains.

Big fish have come out of that water. Springs seep out of the banks, and watercress flourishes in the sodden places where the river and terra firma contest for control. All of it — river, bank and trees — are forest sponge, and through this rolls gin-white water over knobby bottoms.

I saw Hizzoner get down to business with salmon eggs and spinner. I went at it myself with Degerman's recommended Ginger Quill. Oh, there were fish. There are always frying pan fish in this stretch. Mostly rainbows, here and there a brown that forgot to wait until night, and some brooks. In such swift water things can be very exciting with nothing more than a foot of fish on a line.

I saw the good fish — the No. 2 kitchen-sink fish — hit. It was Mister President's salmon eggs he coveted. A rainbow tardy in its return from waters so far upstream. But there was nothing tardy about the way it whacked the salmon eggs. These fish conjure up a kind of electrical insanity when they feel cold steel.

Hizzoner gave it the butt and yelled. I climbed out on the bank and went down there to view the quarrel. It was getting on toward evening. The river chill was rising.

Mister President's rod — the one with the long cork grip to ease the hand — got a workout that day. Above the rapids he yelled, "For the love of ..."

The rest of his conversation was swallowed by river sounds, for it is so noisy in those rips that you can smile at a partner, call him a no-good stiff and he will actually think you are complimenting him. However, I gathered that the President desired that I make a pass at the big rainbow with a little metal-rimmed net which I carried. His own deep-bellied net was back in the canoe.

The fish was a good, standard, spring-run Brule job. Maybe around five pounds. Six pounds, possibly. My net was no instrument for him, but that's what I thought Hizzoner had ordered, and I went to work, all eyes on the fish.

He let him leap, up and down and across. There is no stopping these fellows when they start. Not for nothing do they wear that red badge of courage along the lateral line. When they get tired of plowing the top water, they just lie like stubborn terriers holding to a kid's skipping rope and tug — jerk! jerk! jerk!

Mister President was bellowing over the roar of water. I

did not hear him. I was intent on getting that little net under the fish. The rainbow was brought close. I saw him a few feet from me — a hard, swift bullet of a fish, ready for another dash.

My time had come, and I swooped. I swooped with the net and missed.

Only in nightmares do I recall it clearly. The rim of the net touched that walloper somewhere, and with one powerful twist he was off and away, a shadowy torpedo heading for deep water.

I was a bit downstream from his nibs. I worked back toward him so that I could hear what he had been shouting. Coming closer, I heard: "I was telling you all the time to go back to the canoe and get my net, dern ye!"

That must have unnerved me, for when I got near him a foot slipped. I reached out for support, got hold of Mister President's shoulder and both of us went down.

To this day the Hon. President refers to that stretch as "the place where I swam the Brule, and later hanged a man on a handy cedar tree."

It was too late for a drying fire. There were miles of upstream poling ahead of us. We had the Big Falls to negotiate the hard way. So we got in the canoe and started. Mister President took the rear; I worked a shorter pole in the bow.

Half-way up, I knew we'd make it. We synchronized well as a poling team. The old knack was there. We would both heave with the poles at just the right instant, and get a fresh hold on the bottom at the right time. For once, said I, the Big Falls would find me triumphant.

Only one of us made it, and it was not I. With about ten feet more to go, the canoe gave a sudden and unaccountable jerk, not caused by rocks, you understand. Once more yours truly was overboard. That one, as I recall, was a quick back dive, and while I floundered, waist deep, Hizzoner shot the canoe up the last curling lip of the rapids.

To this day he will admit nothing. He declares such occurrences are part of the hazards of the game. He avers maybe his pole did slip a bit when it should have remained firm, that maybe he did shift his feet just a trifle. But as for admitting he put me overboard — "You know I wouldn't do a thing like that."

It was getting dark when I caught up with him at the head of Big Falls. He was grinning and had his recently filled thermos bottle open and ready for me. I wrung out such garments as I could and thanked the stars for that warm coffee. I raised it to my lips there in the dusk, and I was chilled to the core.

It contained only ice-water. Ice-water! Of which I had recently drunk enough to float the canoe. From the semi-darkness came his voice: "I thought you'd get so hot up here on the upper river you'd need a cooling drink."

Later, while warming with the upstream poling job, he said that once he saved a man's life. The man had fallen in a lake and was well-nigh a goner. He fished the fellow out, squeezed out the water and restored him to consciousness with a hatful of lake water dashed into his face. The fellow came around, said Mister President, ran his tongue over his lips where the water lingered and said, "Dang it, you know I never tech the stuff!"

So we went home with only one kitchen-sink fish, and I was warm as toast long before we got to Johnny Degerman's dock. Which may have been from exertion with a canoe pole, or may have been from listening to the President of the Old Duck Hunters' Association, Inc.

Most of MacQuarrie's characters are competitive, some violently so, Mr. President leading the pack. But it's a soft competitiveness, lacking harshness and bite. Because MacQuarrie's people are all good-hearted people, like Babb here. Winning isn't the only thing. Being a friend and enjoying life is the only thing.

MacQuarrie must have known black-hearted people. There's never been any shortage of them. But they didn't get into his pages or, I suspect, into his life. There was too much warmth and good fellowship to the man. He had it and, mirror like, it reflects in others.

Babb Of The Brule

"Let us stop and wrap this four-pound rainbow around George's neck," said the President of the Old Duck Hunters' Association with a chuckle.

We were returning from a trout opening on Wisconsin's fabulous and fickle Brule. It was dark and cold. Only the hardiest of the spring peepers sang. The northern lights whirled fluorescent banners. The Old Man got the idea of showing George his big fish while he changed socks in the back seat of the car.

"I'm going to show him this fish."

"Your honor," said I, "Babb will have at least two like it, and his wife will have fifteen, none under a foot."

A wet and sandy wader sock swished alongside my ear. "So you won't stop?"

Very soon we were ascending the front steps of George A. Babb's house.

"It's late, darn near ten-thirty," I whispered.

"Knock!" commanded Hizzoner, both hands around that slab-sided rainbow.

Mrs. Babb opened the door.

"Where's George?"

"George!" Her call went up the stairway.

A sleepy "Who is it?" came down the stairs.

"It's Al," she explained. "He's got a fish he wants to show you."

"Tell him." said Mister President, "that I want to show him the kind he never catches"

Her voice went dutifully up the stairs again. "He's come to show you up, George, dear."

The bare feet of George A. Babb hit the floor above. Down he came in his night-shirt, tousled and sleepy, but belligerent. There were no formalities between Babb of the Brule and the peerless leader of the Old Duck Hunters. George said, "Produce your minnow."

The rainbow was slid beneath his nose. George took one contemptuous look and headed for the kitchen. He promised en route that presently he would unveil an open-ing-day catch "fit to take home." He suggested to Mrs. Babb that it was a good time to put on the coffee pot. And he dragged into the living-room, right across the rugs, as mighty an assortment of square-tailed, cold-water fish as this scribe has seen in many a year.

They were in a wash-tub, iced, about two dozen. A few were under a pound. The center of interest was a huge, deep-bellied monster of a rainbow.

"Gargantua!" cried Babb, holding it up alongside Mister President's four-pounder.

"Holy man!" said the President. "It'll go a good five pounds"

"Six and a half!" Babb snorted.

"I guess," said the Old Man, "that I just took in too much territory."

"Like the man who rassled the bear," said George, "you're already yelling 'Stop, or I'll let go!'"

There was vast talk thereafter. George told how he had done it. Salmon eggs and worms with a Colorado spinner early in the day, then big wet flies at midday, and back to bait when the sun rolled under the hill. Mister President managed to issue a few remarks about his own trophy, taken on a black bucktail just below May's Rips. It was a fine meeting until Hizzoner's natural tendencies took charge.

"Tell you what I'll do," he addressed George. "I'll lay you my rod, the one with the 12-inch cork grip, to your waders that next opening night I'll appear on these premises with a bigger rainbow than anything you'll have in that tub."

The hoots of George A. Babb followed us down the steps.

George Babb was perhaps the most proficient fisherman ever to wet a line in the Douglas County Brule. He is the only trout fisherman I know who once announced he would take trout from a certain place, at a certain time, and did it in the presence of a gallery of picnickers.

He came early to the Brule country from Maine. There is a Babb's Island in the Penobscot River of Maine and one in Wisconsin's Flambeau River, both named for logging-day kin of George's. He followed the woods, then took up barbering, fishing and guiding. Although Babb had all the bristly characteristics of a mad porcupine, he had a tender streak in him from here to there. I saw him quit fishing one good evening when accidentally, with a push pole, he knocked a cedar waxwing nest from a tree, drowning the fledglings, while trying to retrieve a hung fly.

He knew the game from A to Z, and loved to disagree with the experts. He had a voice that could boom out a half mile across the Brule's Big Lake. His whisper was a buzz-saw. I am pretty sure that once, for a year or so, he held the world's record for a brown trout, a fish of some 16 pounds, taken about 1916. When a President of the United States came for three months to the Brule, it was Babb who was called on to teach him fly fishing.

This, then, was Babb, a man who would wrestle you for a dollar and a half any day and give you his last chew of tobacco. Homeward-bound, I reminded Mister President that he was about to lose his pet rod. Soothed by Mrs. Babb's coffee and unruffled about the future, he said "If there's a fishin' season next year, I'll win."

"Nuts!" said I.

"Wake me up," said he, "when we hit the edge of town.

I want to get all my gear in one place so you won't drive off with it."

In the long interim of winter I heard reports of meetings of these two. George would come to town once every so often and stop at Mister President's place of business, mostly to promise Hizzoner that he would have that fly rod, come May First. I heard reports of the two of them locked in mortal combat over fishing tactics, though the thermometer stood at 10 below.

One observer relayed that on a street corner where they met one evening he heard Babb exclaim contemptuously, "That old nine-foot crowbar of yours ain't got but the one tip and that's took a set."

To which our peerless leader replied, "Your own wife told me you bought those waders the year Taft was elected!"

On opening day I found myself at 4:30 A.M. driving again to the Brule. The Old Man sized up the look of the country as we drove. He said he liked darned near everything that morning. He liked the way the popples were fuzzy when the car lights touched them. He liked the way the season had come belatedly, so that the big migratory rainbows from Lake Superior would still be in the river. He also liked the way the spring peepers were hollering — "like they had a cheer leader."

"But," he continued, "I do not like George A. Babb this morning."

"You're not running out on that bet?"

Babb Of The Brule

"Me! I'm just mad at him this morning because I'm sure his darn old waders leak. Ere this day is out his hide will be tacked on the barn door."

I had doubts. Had the field of honor been any of a dozen other north Wisconsin streams, I'd have felt safer about Mister President's rod. Babb knew that Brule like the mink that live along its banks.

There was another reason for concern on my part. Mister President, not at all like himself, didn't know exactly where he wanted to put into the stream. It was not time for confusion. The omens were bad. In fettle, the Old Man would have gone to his chosen place as the bee to the honey tree. He speculated as we drove along.

"I'd hit for the Cloquet bridge, only it might rain and we'd get stuck on those hills. The meadows north of Brule might be all right, but there'll be too many there. Winnebojou is a good starter, but since they tore out the South Shore trestle I don't like the look of it ..."

It was breaking day. A decision was in order. No inspired directions came from Mister President; so I nudged his ancient car beyond Winnebojou and down a two-rut road. It's a good place if you get to the end of it with auto springs intact.

He took a long time to get into his waders. He dallied over his gear. He let the leader and line slip back through the guides several times before he had it threaded properly. He asserted that the canned salmon eggs you get nowadays are no good. He exhibited all the insecurity of a lamb getting fat in a feeding pen and not liking it a little bit. It was light when we hit the river.

"I suppose," said Mister President, "that by this time his wife has caught all the trout he needs."

"Who needs?"

"George A. Babb, you derned fool!"

He left me there, preoccupied and, I think, skeptical of this day's luck. I hardly knew whether to laugh or suggest extenuating circumstances, such as substituting another rod for the nonpareil nine-footer. I knew, as Mister President vanished downstream, that up the river some distance the wizard, Babb, was working a magic line over excellent trout water.

True, Mister President might hang a hook in the mouth of a monster. And George might meet up with a bad day. It was unlikely, though.

The only warm praise I can speak for that cold morning is that there were no mosquitoes. Back from the river bank in the little hollows there was crisp ice. My wader boots crunched through plenty of it as I went upstream along the bank.

The river does a good bit of twisting here. In a few places it has tried to cut cross lots. These are hard to get around, harder to wade through. The business of lifting first one foot and then the other from these mucky bottomed backwaters served to warm me up. I came to a place where the stream

144

is wadable down its center, with a deep long groove of water under the left bank. Willows tip over it. Perhaps there was something in there.

The routine was followed in the strict early-season tradition for these waters — worms and salmon eggs with spinners and without, then big gaudy flies, then those black bucktails. After four hours all I had was an empty tobacco can which had housed some splendid worms. The river seemed dead. I grew tired of a fruitless campaign beneath the willows, went ashore, lit a fire and stretched.

The sun climbed. The grass beneath me warmed up. I dozed a bit. Then I was suddenly awake, wide awake, for a man was standing over me, tickling my nose with the slightly dried tail of a six-pound rainbow trout. The man was the President of the Old Duck Hunters.

"I've got him!" he exulted. "His waders are practically hanging in my garage this minute. That big one he had last spring was a fluke."

He related that he had found a hole "and stuck with it." He saw the big one roll and worked on him for two hours — "threw a hardware store at him. Finally I dug around and brought up this little wooden wabbler. Bet I showed it to him two hundred times before he took it."

"And when he took it?"

"Then I says, says I, 'George, if those waders leak, you'll have to pay for the vulcanizing!'"

Mister President was indeed jubilant. The contrast with

his mood of early morning was impressive. He said he felt so darned good that he would climb the steep hill to the car and bring down a frying-pan — "so I can fry up the little ones you got"

I explained I did not have even one little one, that we did not have a frying-pan in the car, and that he was just trying to rub it in.

"Uh-huh," he said. "Got you both licked." Then he rolled over and fell asleep in the sun.

While he sought that repose to which he was entitled I tried again along this favorite water of mine. The warmer weather helped. Wet flies attracted interest. I nailed a few — "half a hatful," Mister President said later. "Ain't you ever goin' to catch a fish too big for a creel?"

In the evening we went up the hill out of the steep valley. He sat on the running-board and I pulled off his waders, a ceremony which concludes with the puller being shoved sprawling by the pullee. He permitted me to take down his rod — "and don't leave any rag-tag bobtail of leader wound around the reel"

I cramped the car wheels to get it out of the narrow turn-around, and we started down the two-rut road. Mister President leaned back with the taste of victory in his mouth and chortled, "Wait till you see Babb's face fall."

All the way the Old Man was drinking hot blood, right out of the neck.

"Oh," he said generously, "Babb isn't such a bad fisherman. He'll have some fair fish under the kitchen sink in that dingdanged wash-tub. He'll be in bed when we get there pretending he's asleep and hoping we won't have the heart to bother him. Can't you push this old hack a bit faster?"

He lifted up his voice in snatches of song. One ballad dealt with how tall the chickens grew in Cheyenne. He also gave a sincere rendition of "The Stars and Stripes Forever." but it seemed to me he put his whole best into "The March of the Cameron Men."

Going up the Babb front steps, he was toting that dangling rainbow and humming, "She'll be Comin' 'Round the Mountain When She Comes." Babb himself opened the door. Mister President got right down to the bricks immediately. "Bring on your fish!" he demanded.

Babb grinned. You knew when you saw his grin that it was an emblem of defeat. He slapped the Old Man on the back and roared: "You've got me this time, cold turkey. I never saw sign of a fish half that big."

"Bring on the waders!" demanded Mister President.

"Put on the coffee" said George.

There was vast talk thereafter. George told how he had done it — salmon eggs and worms with a Colorado spinner early in the day, then big wet flies at midday, and back to bait when the sun rolled under the hill. Mister President managed to issue a few remarks about his own trophy.

The pair of them, well along, gray and grizzled, did a lot of remembering. They went over the history of the Brule from the '90s and the history of Lake Nebagamon from the days when the Weyerhaeusers had their headquarters there. It was late when we left. Babb brought out the waders, still very damp.

"Looks to me like the darned things leak," Mister President sniffed.

"I'll say they do. I gave them a month's wear just today."

"W-e-l-l," said Mister President in a burst of magnanimity, "what do I want with leaky waders? I just wanted to show you, dang you!"

"That you did," Babb admitted.

Mister President went out the door toward the car. I remained behind, for Babb had plucked my coat sleeve. He whisked me quickly to the kitchen. There was the familiar wash-tub, iced. On top of a welter of trout lay a rainbow — such a trout as men dream of — huge, glistening carmine and olive.

"It's nice of you, George," I said before hurrying out to the car. "You know he's getting old."

"Sure, sure," he said. "I am, too."

How many times have we tried something new when all is going poorly? MacQuarrie, fishless, remembers advice from other quarters, floats his dry flies in the fast water and it works! Time after thrilling time! The pupil outfishes the master.

One of MacQuarrie's greatest lines here as well.

"I'll stake my reputation on it," he says.

"Your reputation," returns Mr. President. The woods rang with his laughter. "Shucks, man, you ain't got no reputation. You're a fisherman."

In Quest Of The Lukewarm Beer

"You are an unregenerate backslider," said I to the President of the Old Duck Hunters' Association, Inc.

"You bet your life I am," he answered spiritedly.

"You are," I went on, "a hypocritical rascal without principle or virtue of any kind in your mangy hide"

"Right again," agreed the President.

"One week ago, with a 4-ounce rod and 12-foot leaders, you caught as nice a mess of trout as any man could wish for on a dry fly. Is that correct?"

"Positively."

"And now you hide from my sight on the other side of my car, here on the banks of the Brule River, and hitch up a cast of wet flies on a 6-foot leader for to fish the same"

"Dog-goned if you ain't right, sonny."

"'And you have nothing to say for yourself?"

"Nothing. Only that I am weak. And I love a wet fly. I love to dunk a wet fly and get 'er down in thar where the fishes is."

"And what is that you have on the dropper?"

"That, my boy, is a dog-eared Yellow Sally, about size No. 6, if my eyes ain't gone back on me"

"And the other one?"

"Why, ain't you ever seen a Royal Coachman, No. 8, before?"

"And you're actually going to fish in this low, clear water with that outfit?"

"Yep! I'm goin' right down that path, through them alders, down the steep bank, and I'll hit the crick just about twenty yards below the old bridge. Then I'll wade in about to my stomach and lean back agin' the water and light my pipe while the riggin' soaks up good. After that it's dunk, dunk and dunk again, straight downstream, takin' 'er easy, and by and by something's goin' to take a-holt."

"I hope that fast water bowls you over. Any fisherman, after scaling the dry-fly heights, who resorts to such childish devices ought to drown."

"Don't get flustered, sonny," retorted the President of that revered and august body of anglers and hunters. "While I'm down there doin' things you will be downstream a ways, diggin' in your pocket for that leetle bottle of oil and them there leetle scissors — say, they are cute. And you'll be buckin' the current and fightin' all the fast water and wonderin' where that No. 14 bivisible went after you slung 'er out."

In Quest Of The Lukewarm Beer

"But it isn't all fast water. Some of it is perfect in the still places for a floater, and that's where I'm going."

"Be that as it may," retorted the Association potentate, "I'm goin' to fish wet and big and colorful and traditional. I may be a backslider, but I love the art and science of float-in' 'em downstream and draggin' 'em back — with little jerks, you know."

"Idle banter — mere idle banter," I replied. "And I'll stake my reputation on it."

"Your reputation?" The woods rang with his laughter. "Shucks, man, you ain't got no reputation. You're a fisher-man."

"All right, I ain't. But I've got a bottle of beer in the back seat of the the car."

"Now you're talkin' my language!"

"It's a bet, then, and the pay-off is on trout?"

"I'm off in a burst of derisive laughter," cried Mr. President, and the last I saw of him he was clomping into the brush in his waders in high glee.

It took me longer to get ready, and I had time for thought. The President is not a finished fly caster, either wet or dry. But he's a fish-getter. That previously-mentioned night on the Upper Brule, he had done great damage with my light rod and long leaders, although I could remember no cast that was laid out right. He is a sloppy caster — that's it. But dog-gone it, he gets fish, and maybe he had some-thing up his sleeve this time.

In Quest Of The Lukewarm Beer

I proceeded down an old right-of-way of lumbering days for a scant half mile, made my way through the brush and down the steep bank and hit the Brule just above the old stone dam near the ranger's cabin in Brule State Park, not far from the town of Brule. Ask about it, you fishermen, when you make your pilgrimage to that river. Of course, you will fish this famous stream sooner or later. Everyone does.

I had before me two hundred yards of beautiful dry-fly water before striking the tail of a 150-foot rapids. If I were to get that bottle of beer, I felt it would have to be done in that placid stretch, with just a hint of swirling current here and there. The stream runs north and south at this point.

The east bank is no good. In places there the water is shallow and silty on the bottom. At the west bank, calling for a right-curve cast, there is deeper water, shade and old logs, and you can stand in the middle and work it without wading too deep. The place the President fished was above me some distance, all fast water, as beautiful a stretch of wild, rugged river as you will see anywhere in the Middle West.

It seemed too easy. Good dry-fly water. Twelve-foot leaders with plenty of gut in the first six feet to make 'em lie out, an 8-foot 4-ounce rod delicate as a butterfly's breath but with the kick of a mule as you lift the D line off the water. Yes, it would be easy, I mused as I shook up a No. 14 Badger Bivisible in the "leetle bottle of oil."

Let's see now. The sun is still high and in my face, and

I've got to be careful. But I can get inshore to the right a little and make the shade of the alders. The trout will not see
me so plainly there. It'll be harder casting, though. Too
much line over possible fish, but a little finesse and luck will
take care of that. The bivisible goes on its first looping ride
and settles just above and outside a projecting log. Good. I
know that log. It's deep underneath, where the river has
ducked its head to pass under. The first cast might not do it.
Maybe it will take fifteen or twenty — but no mistakes now,
mind you.

No. No mistakes. And there were no mistakes. Nor were
there any fish. Strange. Always has been good for one. Not
even a rise. Peculiar. Suppose this hot spell has put 'em
down? Can't be possible. It's only early July, and the water is
low but under 60 degrees. They can't all be way down deep.
Oh well, try that run above, toward mid-stream. It would be
a pool if the water weren't so fast at that point. Big rocks in
the bottom. Always a little riffle on top of it. Small fly,
fished carefully along its edge, ought to bring something.

Thirty casts — nothing. Forty casts — nothing. Change
the fly. Try a No. 16 Black Bivisible. It's a pretty bright day.
They may see it better against the blue sky. Many, many
more casts. Nothing. Not even a fingerling. Not even a
bouncing, bumptious dandiprat four inches long where, a
few weeks before, there were hundreds and hundreds of little rainbows, keeping out of the way of bigger rainbows and
browns.

In Quest Of The Lukewarm Beer

Well, that is funny. Gosh, did the President know there was something wrong with my favorite stretch of the river for dry flies that day? What hidden, unwritten lore of the river had he drawn upon to decide against dry flies on such a day? Can it be possible I am ever going to learn to call my shots on this or any stream? Haven't I learned anything from twenty-four years of fishing this river? What's wrong with my fishing? Been reading too many books and not studying the river enough? No, that can't be it entirely. My dope works sometimes — specially the last few years, since I found out that floating flies are fish-getting flies.

I worked the whole of the stretch, but in its entire length saw neither fish nor fin. There was no visible hatch upon the water. Where had they gone? Oh well, try it over. So I plodded back down to the upper side of the dam and went through the same motions. I went through my fly book from top to bottom. I anointed them all with care. I cast them all with the greatest caution. Never, I felt, had I worked so hard to make a fly lie right. And they were lying right. But the fish were not there.

So I sat on the big rock at the foot of the 150-foot rapids and let the sun beat on my neck. It was quite hot, and I was tired. I was also licked. Might hang around until just before dark, but that was too late, and who wants to stumble around in the dark getting back up that hill? No use to go back over that stretch. Could fish it wet, but that's no fun. And that's the only reason I don't like wet flies. Maybe

157

they'll catch more fish sometimes. I just happen to be one of those fool fishermen who like to see a fly float, and so I float 'em.

What to do? What would, say, Mr. LaBranch do? He wrote a book once about the dry fly and fast water. Did he really mean — ? In that kind of water before me? In that sliding, roaring rock-chute up which I must climb to get back to the car the shortest way? He couldn't have meant that. No place to put a fly in that fast water. But is there? By golly, maybe there is.

Now, that choppy little glide just above the water-covered rocks, before she breaks into a froth? Is that kind of water fit for a floating fly? How about dropping it on there and whisking it off before it is dashed into the mixing bowl below? Easy to reach, far as that's concerned. Shucks, a tapered line will be a nuisance in there. Might as well try — it will be an experiment, though. And I never tried for a fish in that tumbling trough before with anything but a wet fly.

Off comes the 12-foot leader, and a 7-footer goes on in its place. It is the shortest I have. A No. 8 bivisible Royal Coachman is twisted on the end, and I shove off the rock into swift water. By standing at the edge I can hold my feet and reach the spot nicely. Seems kind of silly.

Wham! That word is overused but terrifically adequate. No hesitation in that kind of water. The trout saw something buggy and slammed it. Perhaps he hadn't the faintest notion what kind of fly it was. He couldn't have, squinting upward through the small maelstrom that obscured his view. But there he was, and on — hooked himself. Downstream he goes.

The strong and certain pressure of a good fish is thrilling after three hours of such fishing as I had just experienced. I'll get him easy, though. He's hooked good. Just hold him steady and let him run. No! No! Not in to that faster water! It might be too much of a job to hold him there.

The trout decides for himself. He chooses the faster water — and liberty. Pound, maybe, but he felt like two. Can't use a 4x leader here. Take it off and tie on a heavier one. Coarse and over-sized it seems as I jab its point through the eye of another bivisible Royal Coachman. But it will be needed if anything hits again. Wonder if that one was just an accident. Or have I been passing up this kind of water in hot weather for years without knowing it held dry-fly fish? We'll see.

Twenty-five feet above, breasting the snatching current, there is a piece of even faster rapids, but over to my right, just beyond the fast water, is a spot, two feet wide and six feet long, that is comparatively still — so still that at its shore edge I can see down into two feet of water. If only the thrusting river would halt for a minute and let that agitated surface rest, I might see into it. But the river, rushing past, nudges the quieter water with its elbow, and it is moving — rising and falling a few inches. What little foam collects is soon swept away by the vacuum-like pull of the current on the slack water.

A trout should be there. But how to get a fly in there without having it snatched away? I edge a few cautious yards toward it until I am not more than fifteen feet from the spot. Wish I had a level line. The tapered end is too light for a short cast, but it will have to do.

The fly goes out, and the leader has barely settled behind it when the current sweeps it away, leaving a rippling wake. Got to get closer and sneak the fly in from the side and below the hole. Only way I can float it there. I'm not a good enough fisherman to make a real slack-line cast so as to give the fly five or ten seconds of motionless life on the slack water. Five or six casts fail; then a lucky one lies just right, with a little slack. Now if the river will leave it alone a minute ...

Smack! I saw that brown as he grabbed it. He came most of the way out to do it — strange tactics for the deliberate, cautious brownie, but it appears they aren't so careful when they're living in a house with shutters on it such as this one. He's out and downstream — and let him go. He can't smash that leader. He'll soon drown in the six-mile current. It is over quickly. Only 11 inches, but plump and fine.

The two fish I caught took the fly within twenty feet or less of me. So perhaps I can get closer to the next good-looking spot. It is a wave-topped area about fifteen feet square, half pool, half rapids, where the sliding water cruises into heavy bottom rocks and quick little waves are thrown up, to be gathered up quickly in the main flood.

The sun is now directly on the spot, and it is hard to see. Casting is done more or less blindly. I cannot see the fly, but those angry waters are doing things to it, I sense, as the fly remains some time in the area before being swept down to me. Maybe the fly is too small for such water. Better try a bigger one. The aluminum box in my kit avoids my fingers, and I bring up instead another little box. Little bass flies in there. I just wonder ...

So a No. 6 cork body is squeezed through the neck of the fly-oil bottle and then flung into the caldron. At times, on the sun-flecked water, I can get a glimpse of the bright-hued bass bug. It twists this way and that. Evidently there are some strange current forces working on the line and leader, below the surface.

Then the fly disappears in the sun. I raise the rod lightly to see if I can bring it into vision. Instantly there comes down through the bamboo the solid, shaking tremor of a good fish. He might have had the fly in his mouth for ten seconds or so before I knew it. But he's hooked, and I raise the rod higher.

That brings him to life. He darts up through the troubled water and thrusts half his body out. For an instant he is a brilliant, writhing splash of color in the sun. Maybe he saw me, for I am very close to him. He comes down toward me, then out to the right into water that goes strong and swift out of the demi-pool. Easy with him, now. He's a brown and knows what it's all about. Hold him from going over that lip below, and he's mine. The tackle is strong, and I net him before he is half spent, but it is just as well. The bass hook held him none too securely. A good 14 inches. He'll go a pound on a friendly scale.

I have learned something. The Brule seems to chuckle at me as I work up another thirty or forty feet. "Thought there weren't any fish in here, eh?" says the river. "Thought my browns wouldn't take a floater in this water? Ha! Ha!"

But I am satisfied with myself. A new river has been discovered. By accident or pure research I have wrested one more secret from the enigmatic Brule, and the bottle of beer looms close. Should have stuck it in the river, though. It'll be warm in that stifling sedan with all the windows and doors closed tight.

Here's another place. Over on the opposite bank the rushing river has failed to dislodge a two-foot-thick-log, embedded deep into the bank. Behind the friendly shelter of the log the river foam dances, six inches deep, two feet wide. I'll have to keep the fly below that foam. The slack line cast, even with the luck I always need on such a cast, will not do here. The water is too deep and fast for me to get closer than twenty-five feet. How about riding the fly down the edge of the fast water?

I take off the bass bug and tie on a No. 10 Brown Bivisible, for while the water there is swift it is quite glassy.

In Quest Of The Lukewarm Beer

The fly toboggans down the slide a half dozen times before it gets right in close to the stillwater. There it drags a bit, but not much, uncertain whether to join the current or float serenely into the foam on the backwash. The line will decide in a few seconds, when the current bellies it out and pulls the fly down. But a fish leaps into the breach and makes the decision before the river has time to act.

Rainbow this time. A rollicking dynamiter he is, taking the bivisible at the end of a nose dive that is thrill enough in itself to recompense for the whole trip. He makes for the shelter of the log, but ducks out of there quickly to have it out with me, then and there, in the faster part of the current. I seem to detect the added belligerence of the rainbow. But in that water the current is such a strong factor in the fight of the fish that it is hard to tell. I let him winnow down into the spot I have just fished, and there I can feel he has not such an advantage. Ten inches of rainbow, that's all. But it's all fighting fish, and Brule rainbows are heavy-bodied, often much thicker through the middle than browns.

Two more trout — one a brown, one a rainbow — find their way into the creel by the time I am at the top of the fast water. I have five good fish, and I have put back a dozen small ones. Hurrah! I'll guzzle that bottle of limpid beer if it turns my stomach inside out!

There is a place at the beginning of this fast-water stretch where the Brule gently nudges the bank to my right for a distance of twenty feet before toppling into sudden flight down the rocky stairway I have just ascended. I have never caught a fish there. I don't know why, but suspect it is because I cannot make the fly float right. I wonder how it would be to stand right in the beginning of the fast water, at the lip of the pool, and try a cross-handed cast. But to do it I must take off my fishing jacket, else everything in the pockets will be wet.

A new No. 12 Olive Quill replaces the bivisible, and I carefully adjust my feet to the slippery bottom rocks. I can just make it. The water burbles at my wader pocket, but my shoes are wedged solidly into bottom rocks and I can work the fly without danger of the current influencing it. I have been careful. Now I must be more careful, for the cross-handed cast is difficult for me.

A half dozen casts are made with a minimum of disturbance on the still pool in front of me. There is no give-away drag. But there is no response. Maybe I could work it closer to the bank. But to do that I've got to brave the terrors of the brush, and it would end everything if I had to wade into the pool to retrieve a stuck fly. Try it, anyway. Maybe that's why I've never got 'em here before — maybe I've been thinking too much about my precious tackle and have been unwilling to take a chance with a 20-cent fly. For shame!

I feel, as the fly goes forth towards the brush, that I am actually doing something in that spot which I have never before attempted. Will it solve the problem of that pool, which I know must hold good fish but which any fisherman will tell you is good only for night fishing? It will. It does!

The best brown of the day weaves from the shelter of the brush and takes the fly easily. Confident, deliberate, arrogant is he — the perfectly fooled brownie in the quiet pool. Two or three a year is all I ever get of his tribe in that kind of water, but they are worth more than many another taken from less difficult places.

He will not come out, but sulks under the alders. Is he hung up? I pull harder, and he yields. Upstream he goes in the quiet water. I must be careful in getting out of the fast water to follow him, or I shall be swept downstream. Let him run until you get out of this, I counsel myself. There! I gain his own quiet pool, and the sand is firm beneath my feet. What a relief from the uncertain rocks of the stairway rapid!

The brown is ahead of me about twenty-five feet. I have given him line. Now I snub him, and he comes around and downstream directly toward me. I draw my legs close together. How often have hooked fish darted between my waders! He rushes by me at close range and tries for the fast water, but I turn him and back up he goes. Now I've got him. He'll never get into that rapids. I work upstream, to keep away from the fast water. The brown is big, but not big enough to get away in that kind of water. He's mine in a few minutes.

The first fish I ever caught in the pool. Only good for night fishing, eh? And there he is, a good pound and a half.

Fly Fishing With MacQuarrie

Gosh, I'm tired, after that bout with the rapids. Weary legs move toward shore, and I am about to sit on a rock when I suddenly become conscious that I am not alone. I look up. Watching me from the brush is the President of the Old Duck Hunters. He wears a Cheshire-cat grin as he comes through the alders toward me. There is, too, a look of elfish guilt upon his face.

"I've got six, and one will go a pound and a half," I declare without ceremony. "What have you got?"

"Well sir, so help me, I fished this river up and down and crosswise and never got a strike. No, sir; not a thing."

"For once, then, you have been licked." I showed him the trout.

He admitted defeat. It was a great moment for the rank-and-file membership of the Old Duck Hunters. Very seldom is it that the commoners in the organization get the best of the President. But I had done it that day. I had beat him at his own game — at the game he himself had taught me to play.

Such sweet victory comes but seldom in the life of a fisherman. Always there is some old-timer with the patience, the skill and the willingness to show him up. Always that one final barrier to perfection. But today was different. Today I was the victor.

"And now" said I, in the full flush of victory, "I shall climb that hill, pass through the brush at its top and drink the beer we left in the car."

In Quest Of The Lukewarm Beer

Then did the awful supremacy of the President's position assert itself. As one who, by divine right, arrogates unto himself the fruits of the land and the fish of the rivers, he drew himself up and pronounced: "My boy, I cooled that bottle in the river and drank it two hours ago!"

Back to the Brule. This time with spinners and salmon eggs for lumbering steelheads up from Lake Superior to spawn. It's opening day and the stream is crowded with enthusiasts. Fitting that a man of Viking stock should hang one while Mr. President and MacQuarrie look on and cheer. Then there is the ending. Some ending!

Too Dag-gone White

In March, along the valley of Wisconsin's surging river Brule, there is a season, half spring and half winter, when ragged patches of snow linger at the feet of patient gray cedars, though the northering sun beats warmly in the tree-tops. Coffee brown spew, stained from hemlock roots, oozes down the slopes to join the rising flow, and there is a great rushing of waters along the sixty-six miles of the Bois Brule. The old river is on the rampage from 'way up beyond Stone's Bridge clear to the mouth of Lake Superior.

It is a season when discontented fishermen peer petulantly out of windows, beyond dripping eaves, and wonder "if the rainbows are up." When that word is passed, all angling men of parts make haste to get to the river and inspect the annual miracle of 10- and 12-pound fish spawning almost at their feet.

On a windy, warmish-coldish March day 'long about tax-paying time I had occasion to pass the place of business of the President of the Old Duck Hunters' Association, Inc. Mister President was standing in his window with one I recognized immediately as Gus, six-foot-four Norwegian who can and does handle an 8-ounce fly rod as you and I handle one of half that weight. The President hailed me.

"The rainbows are up," he announced, and added hurriedly, "but I can't get down to see 'em till Sunday."

Gus had brought the tidings. He had just returned from the recently dismantled South Shore railway trestle which spans the famous creek near a whistling post and switch block answering to the legendary Indian name of Winnebojou.

"They're up, all right," Gus affirmed. "By yingo, some dandies are laying on the gravel south of the trestle."

Only Gus didn't say it just like that. His Norse accent is something that cannot be reduced to paper. You can sort of play around with that accent, but you can't pin it down. You can give a fair imitation of the way of an Irishman with a word, or a Scotchman, or almost any other good American, but I have yet to see the speech of a Gus set down in black and white in a manner recognizable alike to those who know the Norwegians and the Norwegians themselves.

Suffice it to say that all the good, whole, sound, lusty and gusty Guses pronounce yellow with a "j" and January with a "y." There are other little nuances which this inadequate scribe can only hint at in print. But before we go farther, and to justify and glorify the Guses of this world, let all be advised that when they hear someone saying Yanuary instead of January they should listen closely, for that fellow is more than likely to know a lot about fishing.

There, in the President's garage, the chimes of memory started ringing in Gus' honest head. One thing led to another. Almost before we knew it, Gus was launched on a favorite tale. He began it in the little office of the President's establishment, but half-way through all hands moved into the more spacious showroom to give Gus elbow-room. Striding back and forth among the shining cars, Gus made that tale live and breathe.

Yentlemen, we give you Gus:

"There's just one bait to use in spring. What is it? Salmon eggs. Yudas Priest, what I could do down there today with one yar of salmon eggs and a Colorado spinner! Of course, it being illegal, you won't find me there, by yingo!

"You take a little spinner and throw away the hooks. Put on big bass hooks. Then, when you've got a fish, you've got him — yes-sir-ee. Anyhow, I was going to mention about that day down by the Dry Landing. It was opening day. Six thousand fishermen from Winnebojou down to McNeil's. I had two small ones, but they were — oh-h, about three pounds apiece, and I ain't going home opening day with sardines!

"There's a pretty good hole down there. I came up to it. Yudas! Sixteen fishermen and sixteen poles! Yiminy! I waited. They tried everything. Salmon eggs, spinners, worms, bucktails, streamers. I waited a good hour, and they all left, one by one. Then I stepped in!"

Yentlemen, when Gus steps in, he steps into places where you and I would need a boat. There, in the showroom, we saw Gus easing himself out into the sacred pool, the water gurgling about his barrel chest.

"I knew that hole, all right," Gus continued. "I hadn't fished it twenty-five years for nothing. There I was. Out goes the first cast. All I had on was three salmon eggs with a spinner above. I let 'em slide down to the end of the hole where the water went faster. Nothing. Once again ..."

All this was acted. Not just spoken. Gus strode from car to car. His huge feet thumped the showroom floor. His ruddy face grew ruddier with the zest of impending combat.

"Out I sent it again," Gus went on, eyes gleaming. "Down to the end of the hold. Then — oop! What's that now, eh? Comes on the spinner a little t-i-c-k! Um-hum. So he's there, eh? Um-hum. Yaw. You wait, Mister Rainbow. Me and you are going to do business.

"Third time I cast out and felt the same t-i-c-k. I struck, and nothing happened. A wise one, that rainbow, stealing my salmon eggs. Strategy is what he needs. I put on new salmon eggs and cast again. T-i-c-k.

"Then I got bright idea. Instead of striking, I leaned over ..."

When Gus leans over, it's like seeing the tower of Pisa tip

172

farther.

"I leaned over and let 'em go down in there again —
drift cast. I let 'em go two or three feet beyond where he was
ticking it. I knew the fish would follow so as not to miss
those salmon eggs. I hoped it would work, by yiminy."

You hope so too, as you listen, but you are pretty sure it
will, because Gus has told you the tale a dozen times, and he
tells it so well that people clear away furniture to hear it
again and again in all its primal splendor. There is Gus, huge
arms holding imaginary rod, chest-deep in the flow, swishing between the display automobiles. The air becomes tense.
The moment is at hand.

"Just at the right time I felt the t-i-c-k. I knew he'd followed it downstream. I knew he was turned in another
direction. Right there I gave it to 'im and Yudas Priest ..."

Gus almost went backward over a projecting bumper as
he fought the big rainbow, but he got the trout into the
open between two deluxe models and fought it out there,
even to the point of standing proudly at the end of the fight,
holding the flopping giant aloft in triumph.

Great people, those Guses of the northern parts of our
lake states.

Where you find good fishing you'll find plenty of
Norwegians and Swedes. They excel at the game, either as
commercial or sport fishermen. They are anglers from the
word go, and tough as all-get-out. The kind of lads the Big
Ten coaches smile at when they report in September for the

football team. Plenty of them have lugged the pigskin for Wisconsin and Minnesota and plenty more of them will, by yiminy!

Gus is not only tall but proportioned. He used to fish with a pint-sized pal whom he carried through the deep holes on his back. Legend hath it Gus would stop from time to time and let his comrade whip the waters from this magnificent perch.

Gus departed. Mister President pulled out his watch. It was 2 P.M. He said: "If we jump in the car and run down there right now, the sun will be about right to see the big rainbows either off the South Shore trestle or from the front of the St. Paul Club."

"But I thought ..."

"Never mind thinking. My taxes are due tomorrow. My dandruff is bothering me. My chilblains are peeling, and besides I haven't been outdoors to speak of since last duck season. Come on!"

An hour and a half later the President firmly fastened the single button of the old brown mackinaw and strode forth upon the creaking ties of the ancient trestle to be present at Act I, Scene I of "The Great Rainbow Drama," or "Why Life is Worth Living for Fishermen."

This first glimpse of the big lunkers from Lake Superior in the Brule is one of the Middle West's most dramatic and visible fish migrations. Smelt along the Lake Michigan shores provide another spectacle. Still another is that amazing run of wall-eyed pike up the Wolf River of Wisconsin from Lake Winnebago in April. You can see those newly arrived rainbows as they come up, whereas the smelt only run at night and the walleyes are deep goers. Hence the charm of this Brule spectacle. I have seen at one time as many as fifty persons staring down into the Brule, forty feet beneath them, from that old South Shore trestle.

You first see the fish as mere wavering shadows. The eye becomes adjusted to the riffle, and from a vantage-point you begin to get their outlines in detail. But the "ohs!" and "ahs!" are reserved for the moment when a big, crimson-streaked female rolls on her side and vibrates from stem to stern, apparently hastening the ejection of eggs. Then the startling color of the fish is plainly visible, after which the fish resumes its equilibrium and once more becomes a wavering shadow.

Of course, no fishing is permitted then. Fishing for those big fellows that sometimes lie by the score in a space no bigger than a large room would be sheer murder. Poachers, netters and spearers once reaped a bountiful harvest from the Brule, but vigilantes from game clubs, working with alert wardens, now keep nightly springtime watchers along the stream. One violator got in so deep that he spent a year in the state prison, perhaps as severe a penalty for a game-law violation as Wisconsin has ever seen.

The rainbow run up the Brule is something more than a movement of a splendid game fish. Poems have been written about it. People come from several hundred miles before the season opens to see the big fellows. Natives know it as a sure sign of spring.

This is related so that you may know what sort of pilgrimage called the President from his daily chores at tax-paying time. Right there on the old trestle the season opened for the Old Duck Hunters' Association. Thus it has begun for thousands of north country anglers. It is not for us here, to record the dragging days thereafter, nor the disorderly heaps of tackle laid out for overhauling, nor the endless remembering and the hopeful boastings that ensued between that day and the chill bright dawn of May 1, when the season opened.

It need be reported only that the Old Duck Hunters were there on time, a delicate achievement in itself, made possible by adjusting the get-away with precise calculation of sunrise time and allowing just so many minutes for breakfast, packing and deep prayer. The only delay occurred when the Association halted for a few minutes on a sticky clay road and helped push one of the brethren from a frost boil that had shattered the road's center. That accomplished, no less than thirty cars plunged swiftly through the wallow, labored out the other side and sped off Bruleward. You've got to see that opening-day assault upon the Brule to appreciate it.

There are places where you can escape the multitude, even on opening day. You can, for instance, go in by canoe on the fifteen miles of water from Stone's Bridge to Winnebojou and not see anyone for miles. But because it is canoe water and somewhat inaccessible, by far the great majority prefers to answer the roll call of the faithful in waders. The President voted against a canoe, and we parked with a hundred other cars in a Winnebojou clearing not far from the old trestle. It was Mister President's idea to elbow right in — "Let's try it and have some fun."

The report must be submitted that it was not a great deal of fun at that particular place. One reach of river perhaps a hundred yards long was accommodating twenty or thirty fishermen. Upstream the concourse of fishermen diminished, but it was bad enough. These gatherings do produce fun, however. Everyone knew everyone else, and those who did not soon got acquainted. In such a crowd someone is bound to hook a good one or two, but the Old Duck Hunters emerged from the stream at noon with nothing to show for their labor and planning.

On the sunny side of a twisted cedar the President spread sandwiches, uncorked hot coffee and held council. Halfway through the third sandwich, when I was suggesting we forget the big fellows and go after some fun and small ones on the upper reaches, the President looked up suddenly with more than casual interest.

"On yonder well-worn fisherman's trail," he said, "comes the answer to our problems."

It was Gus. But he was despondent. Even three cups of

coffee, which he drank scalding and straight, and liberal applications of sandwiches did nothing to cheer him. He said he had been "all over dis har river" since sunup. First near the mouth, then at Teeportens, down by Judge Lenroot's and at four or five other places. "... and there's a fisherman on every hold between here and Lake Superior, by yingo!"

Had he seen any good ones? He had, indeed. John Ziegler had one close to ten pounds. Carl Tarsrud had two of them, maybe five and six pounds. Clarence Grace hadn't done so badly. All are sure-fire Brule fishermen. Gus said he had seen maybe fifty rainbows of five pounds or over, "but by yiminy, I can't find a hole that hasn't been tramped."

He said he was quitting; that he would come back the following day, when the opening-day crew had departed. It is a fact that this opening day rush on the Brule fades to practically nothing within a day or two. No Wisconsin stream can match it for the first day. We think the boys like to make a ceremony of it, and then go their many ways on hundreds of miles of other good streams all over the northern end of the state.

Gus was no sooner out of sight when the President swept the luncheon remnants together, grabbed at gear and with his mouth still stuffed urged: "We're following that boy. Hurry! I saw his car over in the grove a minute ago."

No fool, the Hon. President. He explained while we skulked along the trail trying to appear unhurried, that Gus never in his life quit a stream until it was too dark to fish; that wherever Gus was heading now would be all right with us. And furthermore, that following Gus was perfectly legitimate, as also was Gus' attempt to veil his real intent.

All honest fishermen will understand the code. You get what you're good enough to take, with due consideration for bag limits, the folks you are dealing with and your own immortal honor. We watched Gus back out his car and followed along unobserved on a county trunk running parallel to the river.

In the town of Brule, rainbow-trout capital of Wisconsin, where the famous from Presidents Cleveland through Coolidge and Hoover have passed, Gus halted his throbbing engine long enough to clump into Hank Denny's restaurant. From the bulge of his lower lip when he reappeared, we guessed he had laid in a new stock of "snoose" or snuff, if you are unfamiliar with this tidbit. Or, if you are familiar with it, "Norwegian dynamite."

It was easy to trail Gus because of the heavy traffic. He passed the road into the old Banks place and the one down to the N. P. Johnson bridge. We thought he might have turned at these places with the idea of hanging around until fishermen had quit certain holes. But Gus had another spot in mind.

Traffic thinned, and Gus turned left, down a road that we knew well. A road not too safe at that season of frost boils, when red clay seethes and softens.

Too Dag-gone White

Gus must have known it was a long shot he was taking. No one else had braved that road during the day. It was ticklish work. You slide down one hogback and bluff your way up the next, wheels flinging red-clay chunks twenty feet high into the popple trees. At the bottom of a steep hill we found Gus mired.

We climbed out. We gave aid. We spoke frankly of our intentions. Gus laughed. Gus always laughs. With me driving and Gus pushing, we made the hill with both cars, slid down the next descent, and there we were, practically on the bank of the Brule.

"Vell," said Gus, chuckling, as we surveyed the river, "I don't know but what it serves me right to sneak away from you and get stuck."

The Brule at this point, only a few miles from the big lake, was yellowed with red clay washed down from eroding banks that stretch along the river some distance back from its mouth. Gus remarked that a trout could use a pair of glasses to advantage. Murky water has never bothered the President much. He holds it gives an angler an advantage, permitting him to work water more searchingly without frightening fish. All things considered. he'll take a roily creek to one gin-clear, and he's not entirely a bait fisherman, either. In its upper reaches, by the way, the Brule runs gin clear the year round.

The place where we put in is below what is known as McNeil's Hole. The McNeil farm lies along the Brule bottoms. Below a bridge at this point the river bends sharply to the east, then turns again straight north and before caroming off a high bank to the west idles awhile in a long, deep hold.

The Old Duck Hunters love that place. The biggest steelhead I ever saw actually taken from the river came out of that hole on the end of Mister President's leader. It was a seven-pounder. And I mean steelhead, a fish identified carefully later by E. M. Lambert, superintendent of the fabulous Pierce estate upstream.

Lambert knows a steelhead from a rainbow. But he cannot tell at a glance, and neither can anyone else. All you can do is guess. The steelhead is likely to be whiter, but beyond that the boys who know go into the matter by counting scales. However, this is no place to discuss that. There was work at hand.

I went upstream and worked down under the bridge and around the corner with salmon eggs and a spinner. No fun? Well, yentlemen, as Gus would say, "There are times when the water is too damn wet for dry flies!"

I creeled a few small rainbows and worked toward the big pool which Gus and the President had fished. The latter had a nice four-pound rainbow — a dark, deep-bodied, typical Brule rainbow with a pronounced crimson sash down his side. Gus was out there waist-deep, working every thing in his catalogue for another he had seen "roll like a poor-puss, by yiminy"

Too Dag-gone White

"He was white as a ghost," Gus yelled at me from midstream. "Maybe I can get him."

The Old Duck Hunters watched the show. It is always a show to watch Gus. He can wade almost any place on the Brule. That rugged river holds no terrors for him. His powerful legs stand against its brawling push where other legs would wabble and shake. He was using his best formula: salmon eggs and spinner.

You who have not fished the Brule, you who have only read about it, should see it with one like Gus performing in its center. It was getting on toward late afternoon. The warmth of the May sun was being dissipated by the familiar chill that rises from the Brule on the hottest days. Gus stood in almost five feet of water, the yellow flow nipping his wader tops. He nursed the "snoose" in his lower lip and practiced his art.

I saw the fish roll once to the spinner. It was indeed stark white, as Gus had said. A good sign to the layman that it was a true steelhead. The Old Duck Hunters smoked and watched, conscious of imminent drama Finally it happened.

Gus' rod arm went forward and down — he hooks 'em that way. Then the arm was back up and throbbing, and something hard and white and crazy exploded from the pool, forty feet away. Gus backed toward shallow water. The big white fish ran upstream and leaped many times. They will do it before you can think. From the pool came a snoose-muffled roar, such a one as Gus' Viking ancestors might have bellowed in a foray on the Irish coast a thousand years ago.

"Yudas! I got 'im!" he snorted.

To which the President of the Old Duck Hunters added fervently, "Yiminy whiskers, Gus, give 'im snoose!"

Snoose it was in the first, second and third degrees. Of the battle, of the raging to and for, of the unbelievable strength in six pounds of fresh-run steelhead, of the great grunts and snorts from Gus, there is little need for setting down. Suffice it to say the fish took Gus downstream fifty yards, came back into the pool and dogged and bucked and leaped and writhed and rolled on the leader until he was washed up.

All these things have been reported many times. No fish in Wisconsin will exhibit the electric insanity of a hooked steelhead in fast water.

After about twenty minutes there was the ghost-white fish on the tiny shelving sand beach at the edge of the pool, and there were two grand old fishermen shaking hands, and there was an ancient gunny sack extracted from Gus' jacket. Into this the big fish went. The mightiest of Wisconsin trout rivers had once more flashed its beaming smile upon the Old Duck Hunters, Inc.

Indeed, it was a chalky fish. Along the lateral line there was hardly more than the faintest wash of crimson. You looked closely to see it. All the rest of him was white, bluish in places, but white — the sign of the steelhead. A sign we could check later with Emmett Lambert, the Brule's grand old authority, if we so desired. Lambert could take measurements and say what he was. For the present, there was only supreme contentment among the Old Duck Hunters.

Gus dipped a blunt forefinger into the round box and spread a damp layer of snoose under a quivering lower lip. It is something to see a six foot-four Norwegian trembling. Fact is, we were all trembling. And you will, too, if you ever come to grips with one of those Lake Superior submarines. The President got out his omnipresent thermos bottles and passed around hot coffee. His own rainbow, a nice little fish, was forgotten for the larger one.

A native with a long cane pole and a sad look wended toward us from McNeil's bridge. To his hail, "Anything doing?" Gus extracted the still writhing steelhead from the sack and held it high over his head by its lower jaws. The native's eyes popped. He was about to say something when the steelhead contorted in a quick spasm, wrenched free and dropped into the pool.

Gus lumbered toward the fish, scooping desperately. The fish rolled and slithered out of his grasp, and then, with new strength, shot like a torpedo for deep water.

No one spoke for perhaps a half minute. The President's coffee spilled from its cup. I shall never forget the gone feeling that hit me. The native seemed sadder than ever. All eyes were on Gus. For only an instant his face was tragic. Then he grinned. A grin that wrinkled and spread and warmed his great red face and lighted it with something you seldom see on the face of a man in such extremity.

He spoke: "Well, boys, he was a pretty good fish. But damn it, I didn't like his color. He was too dag-gone white!"

To dag-gone white! That from a fisherman who had felt his heart turn a handspring in his throat. Do you wonder why I love those Norse fishermen?

Yentlemen, this reporter begs a last line: When all the fishing is over for Gus, when he will no longer hear the kingfishers screaming along the stream, when all that remains of him is a magnificent legend of a great hearted fisherman, the Old Duck Hunters will write an epitaph for Gus, and this is what it will be:

"Too dag-gone white."

Who among us has not felt the insect's lash? It can be merely annoying. Or it can, as it does here, drive Mr. President from the river.

How did it come that MacQuarrie hit upon this somewhat pedestrian theme for one of his matchless stories? Here's my guess. In his reading he ran across Havelock Ellis' paragraphs in praise of mosquitoes. It put his mind to work remembering the thousand and one times that they made life miserable and he played the pain against the praise using Mr. President as a foil.

Of course, today we have more effective repellants than citronella which wasn't much good anyway and smelled bad. But I can forecast with certainty that even with the latest scientific advances, there will still be times when, like Mr. President, you will leap to your feet and try to swat the little buggers with your canoe paddle.

What! No Citronella?

Let us confront the mosquito problem boldly. The mosquito, as such, appeareth not on the calendars depicting the joys of trout fishing. Nor is he allotted much space in the outdoor magazines, except in the back pages were conscience-stricken department editors in May and June publish Nessmuk's concoction for repelling his attacks.

It may be that trout fishing would be too perfect without mosquitoes; that all must not be balm in Gilead. If fleas are good for a dog because they keep his mind off being a dog, perhaps mosquitoes are good for trout fanatics who drink too often at the well of fulfillment. Good golfers have handicaps. Why not, then, mosquitoes for trout fishermen?

The President of the Old Duck Hunters' Association, Inc., showed me, one night on the Brule, the heights of madness to which mortal man can be driven by mosquitoes.

Mister President went with me that evening to the upper reaches of this amazing creek, and when the wind died with

189

the sun we discovered we were without mosquito dope. Not even a smell of any brand or variety did either of us possess, and we were a full hour by slow canoe from our car and immunity.

The pests poured out of the woods just as the big browns began sidling into the open runs where a fellow could get at 'em. They advanced in ragged but determined formation upon our juicy flesh, their deliberate daggers shooting us with the well-known fury which surely must be distilled in sheerest hatred. Squadron A, led by an old hag with streaming hair and yellowed fangs, forced into a mackinaw jacket. I dug up a raincoat, but my head and hands were unguarded.

Hizzoner was handling the boat. He has, at times, a Job-like docility. This was one of those times — for a little while. But courage against mosquitoes is folly. Slow, itching death is infinitely the worst of tortures. As valor waned in the rear seat I could feel the stout canoe frame vibrate as the harassed Mister President sought to stem the invasion.

The choosiness of a brown out front kept me fairly well occupied, although my chores included a constant, mechanical brushing of face and hands as I cast. The insects were so thick that with one brush along my coat-sleeve I could kill fifty. A wet spring and sudden warmth had hatched this baleful brood. The worst ever, all agreed. Farmers in the fields laid down their tools and stole behind screens that season.

What! No Citronella?

I took a glance backward. The once proud leader of the Old Duck Hunters was a sorry spectacle. A devilish horde of bloodthirsty insects encircled the gray of his head, just below the hat brim. Frantic scratching had made his neck and jowls a red and white horror. Even in the heavy smoke of a cigar the countless demons hovered and hummed.

Suddenly, in a paroxysm of fury, Mister President leaped to his feet in the canoe and with one long, desperate shudder began flailing the air with his paddle. There was something splendidly courageous about it the first few seconds. He flailed about unmercifully, like Hector at the bridge, but unfortunately he was in a canoe, not on a bridge. Finally — game to the last — he went overboard.

The water was about two feet deep, but Mister President embraced it in a horizontal position; so it might as well have been six feet. I then installed in him the bow, with the belief that the activity of casting would allay the agony. In the stern I soon found just how much worse these pests can be without something to occupy one's attention. It was truly awful. The hum of their hunger filled the still night air like a paean from hell. All about us trout rose, smashing recklessly at a hatch of other insects.

It couldn't last. We were licked. When Hizzoner began to bleed, he decided it was time to go. He is particularly susceptible to the bite of a mosquito, but strangely is comparatively immune to the no-see-um, which drives me wilder than a dog with a can on his tail. To leave all that fishing and bend to pole and paddle was heart-rending, but so harassed were we that fright gave us wings as we breasted the slow current on the back track.

It is a fact that we were just a little hysterical as we disembarked, tied the canoe and dived into the car. Tackle was tossed into the rear in an unassorted jumble. We flung the car into the breeze with windows wide open and fled, posthaste. That, my friends, was the only time I ever knew of Mister President's being chased from any trout stream.

On a hill we stopped the car and stowed our gear. We considered running into town for a bottle of citronella, but Hizzoner doubted if Charlie Blaxall would have any more than a quart of it and he hesitated to return with anything short of enough for a complete bath. So we headed homeward, and Mister President climbed, with many a mutter, into the rear seat to straighten things out.

"Man's a fool ... Never get me out there again for a month ... Don't know why I chase trout when I could get some good walleye fishing with half the trouble ... All trout fishermen are fools anyway ... Lord, but my neck is burning! ... !

Translated, that means "Let's go back tomorrow night," which we did.

Mister President had a full pint of citronella, and I was equipped with Nessmuk's lotion and an old shirt, without which said lotion is no good, as it's death on clothes.

This time we abandoned the far upper reaches of the

What! No Citronella?

Brule, and I set Mister President in the river half-way between those two famous bridges — Stone's and the Winnebojou wagon bridge. He had waders, an anchor and all needful equipment for the eight-mile trip that lay before him. His plan, in such cases, is to drift and cast, tossing out the anchor when he wants to stay a while. Not very good for dry flies, but all right for dunkers. If he felt swayed by the classic mood, he could oil up his dry flies and get in with the waders, after snubbing the boat to the bank.

I was to go below to the wagon bridge, over which a wagon hasn't rumbled very often since the auto came along, do my fishing there, and then pick him up at ten o'clock P.M. This is a good pick-up spot. There is a rollway up which two willing fisherman can drag a boat to the waiting trailer. The water thereabouts is not bad. I deposited Mister President at his putting-in place and departed for the downstream rendezvous. It was going to be a good night, muggy and promising.

I parked the car with trailer in a safe place, donned waders, old shirt and Nussmuk's axle grease and set to. About my fishing there is nothing to report except that I worked downstream a mile and back without catching anything, and then grabbed a pound brown out from under the bridge, not fifty yards from where I put in. It was nine o'clock P.M. by that time; so I settled back with my pipe in the car, all windows closed to keep out the ubiquitous mosquito.

Fly Fishing With MacQuarrie

I rummaged in the side pocket of the car for reading matter. A road map with routes to a new trout stream, extra fuses and a large bottle of something were pulled forth. The bottle — you've guessed it — was Mister President's citronella! I stared at it unbelievingly and, it must be said, with fearful misgivings. Eight miles down the Brule in mosquito time, part of the way through rapids in the dark, and no citronella!

The complete horror of such a situation can hardly be appreciated by you who sit at home reading this. To get its full meaning, one must have had recent and fulsome contact with Brother Mosquito at the height of the mating season, which seems to extend to about mid-July here. And Mister President, clean-shaven, ripe for plunder all the way down that eight-mile horror! What must he have thought when he reached into his warbag for the dope and found it missing! What would he say? What could he do?

And then — horror of horrors! — I suddenly remembered that, just as I had turned the car and trailer at the putting-in place, I had seemed to hear someone yelling at me. Yes, I had! Someone had yelled, but the car windows were shut and I thought I imagined it. It had been the President, who had suddenly noticed the absence of the ointment and had shrieked at me to stop. I'd better not mention that I had heard — and him with a tender skin.

There was nothing to do but wait. Time passed. The whippoorwills whipped. The tree-toads treed. The katy-dids did. I rummaged through the side pocket again and found a little magazine. On one page were three paragraphs entitled "Eulogy of a Pest," by Havelock Ellis. A fitting tribute, indeed. Listen:

"To the mosquito has been given a greater part on the stage of the world's human history than to any other creature. Down the minute microscopic groove of its salivary gland 'has flowed the fluid which has closed the continent of Africa for countless centuries to civilization,' and which has played a dominating part in destroying the civilizations of ancient Greece and Rome.

"Yet there is nothing more fragile or in reality more beautiful than the mosquito. We have been almost as blind to the loveliness as to the deadliness of this fairy creature whose delicately alighting feet are unfelt by our rough skins. For its beauty is a function of its deadliness. Those huge emerald eyes on the dark background, those iridescent and transparent wings, the double-edge sword of its long tongue, the slender legs yet so mightily strong — all are needed to pierce swiftly and silently, with the maximum of force and of skill, the heavily armored epidermis of man.

"So that if you would see all of nature gathered up at one point, in her loveliness, and her skill, and her deadliness, where would you find a more exquisite symbol than the mosquito?

Not bad, not bad. A pretty piece and worth reading twice.

Fly Fishing With MacQuarrie

Outside the car windows I saw the hungry horde zooming in countless numbers. Ten-thirty came and went. I made quick trips from car to bridge to see what might be coming down from upstream. A body, maybe — or an empty green boat. Mute evidence of what the "microscopic glands" might achieve in the case of one driven to desperation.

At eleven o'clock the dark river yielded forth sound, about a hundred yards upstream. The sound was a very good representation of a mosquito-tortured human trying to get a boat off a rock. A paddle grated. There were grunts. Yea, there was more. There was cussing. Cussing in all its primeval nakedness, stripped of apology, now deep and sad like the low moaning of a lost soul in Hades, now loud and shrill.

It was, of course, Mister President, homeward bound. The sounds came rapidly nearer, and in the darkness I saw him frantically paddling down toward me. I called, and at my shout he answered with a feeling that even Shakespeare would have applauded:

"No longer mourn for me when I am dead. Then you shall hear the surly sullen bell. Give warning to the world that I am fled From this vile world, with vilest worms to dwell!"

Down the bank I scrambled with a flashlight to light him on his way.

Under the bridge he shot, the boat leaping madly to his paddle. I grabbed its prow as it touched the bank, and without a word we dragged boat, fishing rods, tackle and all up the rollway and lashed it to the trailer.

"Just don't say anything, but start driving with the windows open," directed the President.

In the flashlight he was a sorry, tortured figure. Again the itching welts of red and white covered face, neck and hands. His eyes gleamed wildly in the light from the instrument board as we drove homeward. I handed him a tube of lotion of high virtue for such afflictions, and he smeared himself thoroughly. Then he spoke:

"Of course, I should kill you. Not quickly or painlessly. No, that would be too good for you. I should lash you to a spiky spruce at sun down — naked — and let the mosquitoes have their way. Didn't you hear me yell at you? I shouted my head off."

"I didn't hear a word," I lied.

"You knew that citronella was in the side pocket, right where I tucked it when I bought it in the drug store."

"So help me, I didn't."

Had he caught any fish?

Yes, a half dozen pretty fair ones — one nearly a pound and a half — but he'd lost all interest in fishing after the boat capsized in the Wildcat Rapids.

No kidding?

"Yep. I had the flashlight in my hand to pick out the course, and she hit a rock and went sidewise quick as scat. As she heeled over I grabbed the gear and held it. I didn't get

197

very wet — only up to my chin. You really can't call that wet. I got her straight, bailed her out and off the rock and kept on goin'.

"Word had been sent down-river I was coming. I'm sure I saw signal fires on the hills. The farther I went, the thicker the mosquitoes were. It reminded me of the stories I used to hear back in Canada of the gathering of the clans in Scotland after a Campbell had shot a MacGregor for stealing sheep.

"Passing down through Big Lake, I went through a convention of traveling salesmen mosquitoes. They must have been traveling salesmen, because they all picked right up and came along with me. Through Lucius Lake me and the drummers struck up an agreement. They helped me change flies if I let 'em stay on until they were full."

The soothing salve of the mosquito cream had penetrated Mister President's skin, and he warmed to his narration.

"In that rapids just above the wagon bridge we had it out. They sensed I was getting away on 'em and called in all the bombing planes from the hangers in the spruce trees. Under the railroad bridge they almost got me when the boat went sidewise again up against the timbers.

"I thought of drowning — there's a convenient eight-foot hole right there, just below that rainbow spawning bed. But a whim of the current saved me, and I struggled from their embrace as the boat swung endwise and backwards downstream. I just let 'er go and swung the paddle around my head to keep 'em off. Every time the paddle hit one you'd hear a sound like a paper bag full of water busting. That was my life's fluid ebbing out of 'em. If it had been daylight, you'd have seen the water run red down where you were."

Truly, Mister President was doing very well, even for Mister President. He really is so literal-minded that once when I crept upon a pot hole and called to him, "There's a million ducks down here," he came up and whispered back at me, "Hell, you're crazy. There's more'n that. There's a hundred!"

We reached home and switched on the dome-light. The little magazine with "Eulogy to a Pest" came to hand as I reached into the back for our gear. It was too much to resist. I read:

"Those huge emerald eyes on the dark background ... the double edged sword of its long tongue, the slender legs, yet so mightily strong — all are needed to pierce swiftly and silently ... the thick and heavily armored epidermis of man. So that if you would see all nature gathered up at one point ... where would you find a more exquisite symbol than the mosquito?"

"Where?" asked Mister President, innocently enough as he reached for something.

"There!" he said joyfully as a wet, sandy wading sock plastered itself over my face with a soggy swish.

Stowing something away ... then forgetting where you stowed it. Common fabric of human life. In this case it's fishing tackle. Mr. President's fishing tackle. Except when you lose something you probably don't stop friends on the street and accuse them of stealing it. Or enlist the aid of a detective even if he is an old friend. Or surreptitiously check the creels of your fellow anglers trying to catch "the monster in human form."

Mr. President does all those things and more. Not because he lacks fresh tackle. His buddies rally to supply him anew. No, the cause for alarm is a familiar one. The missing flies and reels and lures and leaders are old pals. They are tried and true. They have earned Mr. President's confidence. How can you replace the irreplaceable?

You can't. Nor can you ever replace this irreplaceable old man.

The Mystery
Of The
Missing Tackle

This is about the President of the Old Duck Hunters' Association, Inc. and the ten months he lived in a clothes closet.

At first the tale was just so much idle gossip in Superior, Wisconsin, barber shops. That early version said the President dwelt in the closet only by night.

But lusty souls of that far northern city went to work on it, polished it, gave it life and that necessary emphasis which has caused it to survive throughout the years.

In its amended form Mister President was depicted as spending the entire ten months in the closet, presumably wandering with gun and packsack, living off the country, making his bed where night overtook him.

Far be it from me to amend or delete the folk lore of Superior. I have too much affection for the city that gave me birth and the Brule river only thirty miles away.

The Brule river really started the whole thing. The Brule river and four handfuls of trout fishing tackle.

The President was sitting in his living room. It was early March. Outside, a tardy blizzard off Lake Superior was lashing empty streets.

He leaped out of his chair suddenly, muttered "I wonder if it's there," and ran upstairs, his wife told me later.

She heard him ransacking the large closet in his bedroom. She can tell when he's doing it because he takes a broom handle and sweeps everything off the shelves. Things thump on the floor. He goes through the debris without having to stand on tip-toe.

He came downstairs and told her "It's gone!" She said, "What's gone?" He said "Four big fly boxes, three leader boxes, a fisherman's knife, four loaded reels ..."

She said, "Here it is March and the season won't open till May. Begone!"

The upshot was that she joined him in a second search of the suspected closet. He felt vaguely that he had done something with it the previous autumn. He said he had an idea he put the stuff somewhere, like a squirrel stores nuts — "some place where I could put my hands right on it."

He was urged to put his hands on it then and clean up the mess in the closet, but he was so preoccupied he could do neither.

That was the beginning of the Clothes Closet

The Mystery Of The Missing Tackle

Expedition. The search eventually included the whole house and extended through days and nights, weeks and even months. The neighbors lent a hand at times. A high spot in this friendly assistance was reached one night when they found two bottles of forgotten blackberry wine in an old trunk.

The President got so he could specify the losses glibly. At first the search was confident. Later it went into the suspicious stage when he began suspecting people of stealing the missing tackle. The week before May 1st was an especially trying one. The Salvation Army, the Good Will people, three innocent neighbors and an equally innocent old clothes man were charged with the crime.

The list of departed treasures appeared at headquarters on a police report spindle.

The missing tackle was indeed no ordinary kit of fishing instruments. Each and every fly, wet, dry and streamer, was a cherished classic. There were such carefully distributed baubles as John Ziegler's hand-made black bucktails; several sparsely-tied delicacies of proven worth and scores and scores of others, each of which reminded the President of victory or defeat on the trouty battlefields of North Wisconsin.

The third or acute stage occurred when his sense of loss turned to desperation. That was the evening before the season opened. During this phase he knew it was a plot against him. Even when three suspected neighbors came in and loaned him enough tackle for the morrow his faith in mankind was not wholly restored.

You couldn't get him away from the big clothes closet. He didn't know why, but he was darned near certain "that's where I put it last fall." Often he would stand on the threshold of the closet, poised, hopeful, then go through it automatically, like a combine through a North Dakota wheat field.

However, immediate needs were well supplied by the accused neighbors that opening eve when I came over to pick him up. He had his own rod, waders, in fact, all of the larger items of his tackle. These, with contributed flies, reel, leaders, and what not, left him fairly well supplied with equipment.

On the season's first trip up that way anyone in his right mind and in striking distance goes to the Brule. After a night near the river, during which he thought up new places to look when he got back home, we put in downstream.

I recall it as an exceedingly good day. But Mister President's attention was divided. He would sight a friend from afar, climb out of the pool he was working and accost him on the bank with bluff and deceptive friendliness. While he engaged his fellow man in casual conversation his roving eye took in every item of said fellow man's equipment. I don't know how many creels he thrust his hand into, how many fishermen he secretly inspected, how many parked cars he peered into.

The Mystery Of The Missing Tackle

A police detective had told him maybe the thief had peddled the tackle to some unsuspecting comrade. Following each inspection he would return to the stream and go about his chores until another suspect hove into sight.

It is not to be supposed all this work was conducted in a dead silence. Mister President was prepared at any moment to deliver a speech on "the monster in human form who crept into my house and robbed me."

"It ain't," he would say, "that I object to the financial loss. It's just that it can never be replaced. I haven't got confidence in these other flies. Take that old yellow Sally I used to keep in the upper right compartment of the big box. That's caught more native brookies than they've planted in this state in the last year.

"Yes, a yellow Sally. A bass fly, if you please, that I never used on anything but big native trout late in the evening. Worn out? Not on your life! No hackle left on it, if that's what you mean. And the body was unraveling and the wings chewed.

"No sir, that fly was just in the prime of life. Round about the time when the first deer were snortin' in the brush, anxious for a drink after a hot day, I'd lay that yellow Sally up against the undercut banks and — socko!"

Still, the first day was one to remember. The Hon. President, even without his precious talisman, creeled a likely mess of good ones and wound up with a five-pounder. Even with this deep-bodied rainbow, tail projecting from his creel, he was loath to admit the virtue of the lure that had done it. It was a small fly rod plug, miniature replica of a larger cousin of bait casting persuasion.

"It took everything I had to make him hit," he explained. "I knew he was there because I'd seen him roll. It took me an hour to make him hit it. Now, if I'd had ..."

The self-same plug, to all human eyes except those of Mister President, was the identical gadget he had used in his own kit.

That evening, driving home, he suggested maybe it would be a good idea to move into a new house, because you find a lot of lost things when you move.

It was an angler's evening. The western sky was drenched with red. The roads, though rutted, were dry, a boon indeed to opening day fishermen along the lower Brule. It was an evening to count oneself fortunate with half the weight of trout we bore home. The President said:

"If I move I can stand at the door to keep an eye on the movers."

When the fish were laid out on the kitchen sink to be witnessed, the President omitted his customary proud office of detailing the struggles, each and every one. The visiting neighbors gaped by themselves while he made a couple of swings through the clothes closet.

Things went on that way. There was that day on the Marengo, below Ashland. with the water up two feet, a new batch of Emerson Hough's donated by Ray Schiller gave the lie to those who hold that your brown trout is no fellow to seek with a wet fly, downstream. It seemed to make no difference how you presented it that fine foggy day on the bankful Marengo. The clipped deer hair body with its simple faint wisp of hackle, running deep, medium or on top, stood the Marengo browns on their heads.

It was another day for the books, as was revealed when the car headlights were turned on at evening to illuminate three damp, glistening creels of brown trout. The car bumped and wound away from the rocky, fog-bound crags. Schiller asked me how I liked the Emerson Hough. Before I could reply the President put in:

"Didja ever try a No. 6 Ginger Quill or Hare's Ear in water like that? I used to have some beauties. Someone stole them ..."

Schiller was sympathetic. He offered replacements from his own stock, but the President decided he could accept such largess only as a last resort — "I'm gonna get that crook if it's the last thing I do."

He was convinced now that the disappearance of the tackle was sheer larceny, the work of some venomous rascal, planned with cold malice to make his days unhappy.

I do not recall a summer when the trout rose more steadily to our flies in an assortment of streams. There were some empty days. At such times the presidential faith in his own departed gear was strengthened. "Now, if I'd just had those little gray midges when the trout were tailing there

tonight ..."

It was a year of copious rains, not too hot, so that trout
were not so prone to seek the inaccessible headwaters. A year

when threatening droughts were banished by freshening rain and streams ran healthy and bankful right into September.

One day on the gin-clear Clam, of Washburn county, the President almost forgot himself. The Clam, to ye who know it not, can be as sweet as a piscatorial problem as you'll find. You see the big browns ahead of you. They look easy — but they aren't. In the time of the shad fly hatch when they go smashing along the surface with mouths open saying *"Yaw-skumsh!"* They can be had. At all other times their taking is difficult in the extreme.

That day, a cool, heaven-sent Sunday in the midst of a brief heat wave, the President covered himself with glory via a brace of brown spent-wings which spread their unselfish selves on the unruffled Clam most advantageously. That day indeed was heard again the *"Yaw-skumsh!"* reminiscent of shad fly time.

And sitting in the shade of a giant elm at noon with the appetites of honest, hungry men, the President relaxed long enough to finger the spent-wing that hung from his leader.

"That one is sheer poison," he praised. "I gotta get some of those."

He stopped there. Whatever tribute he may have added died a-borning when the lost tackle came to mind. He sighed over a cold beef sandwich and hoped whoever swiped his tackle would come to an unhappy end.

There was that day on the smallmouth end of the

Fly Fishing With MacQuarrie

Namakagon when one of those plop-plop bugs with a hollow head did all that anyone could expect a bug to do. It didn't exactly swim out and grab any three-pounders in back of the ears, but it had some of them leaping out of the shore growth and timber tangles like kids after a balloon salesman on Sunday afternoon in the park.

Did the President then renounce the long-mourned treasures of his bosom? He did not! He said that one of John Ziegler's mystic black bucktails would have been just the thing that day.

From time to time, coming and going, fishing and getting ready to fish, in boots and in boats, the President pronounced:

"Everything a fly fisherman needed was in those boxes. Anyway 200 flies. Some I had since I was a kid. Wet flies you could sink without rubbing them in the mud. Dry flies that floated if you just let them smell the cork of the oil bottle. The accumulation of a lifetime. And where are they now? Maybe languishing in some far distant pawnshop."

"With a price tag of four bits on the whole outfit," I added helpfully.

"It may well be," he would conclude with ineffable sadness.

Even far into the duck season His Honor carried the burden of his loss and forever he probed the now well-nigh impassable depths of the clothes closet. He would look at the door of the closet, scratch his head and draw thumb and forefinger over the edges of his mouth in thoughtful pre-occupation.

Neighbors inquired from time to time how things were going. The chief of police asked him how he was coming with his detective work. October passed into November, but long before Christmas relatives had decided to do something for him on the Yuletide.

It was the custom of the President to observe Christmas in whole hearted fashion. A circle of fishing relatives invariably convened at the President's home Christmas Eve. Such gatherings were more than fitting family conventions. They were down-right profitable gatherings for the fishing tackle makers.

Always there was a Christmas tree, about the lower branches of which reposed gleaming plugs, reels, knives. A Christmas without these things was no Christmas at all to that crowd.

Christmas Eve came 'round and the faithful came and sat and exchanged fishing tackle, socks, flannel shirts, etc. as has been their wont these many years. Mister President's gifts were practically all fishing tackle.

When the last bit of crumpled tissue paper and bedizened ribbon had been picked up, when the under parts of the Christmas tree looked like a sporting goods window in May, Madame President gained the floor. She said she had an important announcement.

"I have," she said with weighted pauses, "found the fishing tackle!"

"Where?" The words rang out like an angel's chorus. The President leaped to his feet. Madame President bade him be patient.

"Just you sit there a moment," said she. "You have accused everyone in this house and everyone in the neighborhood of filching your old tackle. You ought to be ashamed."

The President sank back into his seat.

"Further," she continued, "you have made a shambles of my house. You have practically wrecked that clothes closet for one thing. Aren't you ashamed?"

Mister President hung his head in abjection, but by leaning over a little bit I could catch the gleam in his eye. Finally he made bold to ask Madame President where he might find the tackle.

"I'll lead you to it. I'll lead everyone to it!" she announced.

Eleven people trooped behind her upstairs. She halted before the clothes closet door. Mister President gasped: "Not there!"

"There indeed!" she said. She switched on a light and the havoc wrought in a ten-months' search was made visible to all. Ladies said "Dear me!" Men gazed with envious wonderment.

Hunting and fishing paraphernalia without end was strewn about. It is a big closet, as I have said, but the only way you could get into it was by wading through packsacks, guns, tackle, sweaters, shell boxes.

Madame President thrust in an arm and lifted from a hook near the door a pair of old, worn, stained khaki trousers, one pair out of a half dozen which had outlived their usefulness. The trousers had been obscured on the hook behind a variety of other outdoor clothing.

Both legs bulged like bags. Around the cuffs were tied old neckties to close the bottoms. She shook the pants, holding them aloft for all to see. From the depths came the clink of metal against metal. She upended the pants and poured out on the floor every last item in the late lamented list of tackle. The President said "Well, I'll be damned!"

Madame President said, "Right where you put them a year ago last fall. It was that day you wanted to use your fishing jacket for a shell vest because it was warm. Remember?"

The assembled witnesses yipped. They slammed the Honorable President on the back. They suggested he get in there and tidy up the closet.

His treasures restored, the President regained some of his old form. He piled the tackle neatly and picked up the pants.

"H-m-m-m," he said, inspecting the knots. "Dirty work after all. These knots are granny knots. Everybody here knows I always tie jam knots!"

"Well, then, you would know how to untie a jam knot, wouldn't you?" demanded Madame President.

"That I would," His Honor answered.

"Good! After you get through straightening up that clos-et untie this jam knot!"

She encircled his shoulders with the pants and knotted them firmly under his chin.

We've all created our treasured relics. A favorite plug or, in this case, a found wet fly takes fish after fish. But each time the struggle of the fight taxes the fly. MacQuarrie uses a prize fighter analogy. The fighter wins but each round takes more and more out of him.

Finally, its wings askew, hackle gone, hook bent, shank showing, MacQuarrie tucks the McGinty in his fly book. But every time his eyes rest on the battered old veteran, it will transport him back to the river "musing thoughtfully under the deep banks and purling quietly in the swifter places."

Down Went McGinty

I found it firmly stuck in a bushy branch — that warrior McGinty fly — after I had waded precariously through the deep hole over which the branch drooped. It wasn't my McGinty until that moment. My own fly had fastened to the same branch and when twitches failed to loosen it I hitched up my canvas jacket to protect the camera in its pocket, and, like an old lady crossing a muddy street on a rainy day, made my way slowly through the pool.

The pool, ordinarily, is not to be waded but the Brule was low and I barely made it, with only a trickle slipping over the wader top and darting down my leg to prove once more how cold the stream can be. It was getting late even then and I groped to locate my marooned Coachman. My hand felt a fly and I twisted it out of the bark. It was Mr. McGinty himself — yellow vest, black waistcoat, red socks and all. I retrieved the Coachman, made a retreat out of the pool, and sent forth grateful acknowledgement to Chief

Fly Fishing With MacQuarrie

Winnebojou and the aboriginal headmen of Wisconsin who are supposed to look after things on the Brule.

"If this," I ruminated, "isn't a sign from above, nothing is."

Three hours before I had donated my last McGinty to the gentleman I was fishing with, and from all indications he was using it with wonderful results. He had offered to give it back when he creeled his fourth rainbow and I was still tying and untying Turle knots on flies they wouldn't even smell. I had made some foolish remark about "that bee never catching anything anyway," and I didn't want to back water.

It had been a remorselessly hot day. The Piscatorial Prevaricator and I had chosen the afternoon to penetrate a relentless jungle in quest of favored waters. Sopping with perspiration we had plunged into the river where the regrettable transaction took place. He had set off upstream with it, fishing it wet and I followed, one hundred yards behind, using dry flies, wet flies, and Republican flies, which are neither wet nor dry, but only get a little damp and dry out in the first good breeze.

When I passed him, upward bound myself, he reported the McGinty's record.

"I'd give it back in a minute if you wanted it," he said.

"Oh, keep it, that's all right," I replied. "They must be taking something else."

"Sure, they must be, they must be," he came back, rather

hurriedly, I thought, and added, "They're taking it if I can get it down far enough to 'em. Can't whip it much but gotta let it soak and get good and wet. Then they hit it. It's tied right for a deep wet fly, too — not too much hackle on it. Just like the McGinty in the old song — you know, 'Down went McGinty to the bottom of the sea'."

He actually attempted to hum a few bars of the song and there I left him, the ingrate, and it was not until the McGinty of the pool came in to my life that I felt the slightest flicker of that hope which stirs honest fishermen to further crusades.

As I was saying, it was growing darker. If I were to come in that night with anything I had to set to work right away and the fading light discouraged more tying and untying. It was Mr. McGinty or nothing. He had to go down and come up with something if his latest owner hoped to overcome, with fishy spoil, the taunting thrusts of his companion. I thought of Casey at the bat, not forgetting his woeful failure, but McGinty came through in such a way as to more than wipe out the blot against the immortal Casey. It seems a fact that what one Irishman can't do, another one will, and between them they can do almost anything.

Now for the fishing. The Brule at evening. Mellowed, waning light pouring down through the pines, revealing the stream with a gentle gray delineation like a perfectly exposed photographic negative. A persistent fiddling of crickets. Here and there an early firefly with his lantern aglow. A white throat saying the same old thing over again, and the river itself, musing thoughtfully under the deep banks and purling quietly in the swifter places. The magic dusk seems to lay a hand on the impulsive current, as though to stay it, for a moment, in its short but tumultuous, journey to Lake Superior.

It had to be downstream fishing from then on. The homeward route lay that way, and I was compelled to take it, although I would have preferred to proceed farther upstream and work Mr. McGinty like a dry fly, letting him drift down to me. But I had to make the best of things.

Mr. McGinty — I think he was a No. 10 — sailed out over a little pool, one of those baby pools where the stream nudges the bank coyly, and only hesitates before continuing on to linger for a real caress in a deeper, stiller pool. On the Brule there are "holes," which are not so idyllic but just as descriptive. Mr. McGinty, with characteristic Irish stubbornness, fastened himself in an overhanging branch, but a slight movement released him and he fell into the water with a little splash. I had soaked him well and he floated for hardly an instant before making his dive to the bottom, or thereabouts.

I tell everyone who asks — and many who don't — that the trout that went after McGinty was eighteen inches long. He struck like twenty-four inches and Mr. McGinty hit right back, a sock in the teeth that fastened the brook trout for good. He put up a noble contest. Mr. McGinty hung on, through thick and thin, fast water and dead water, but it was a lot darker when I finally slid the net under his beaten victim. An eighteen-inch brook trout — is there any fish so beautiful, so symmetric, so perfect in all respects? All honor to the browns and the hell-for-leather rainbows, but the native American trout in his own bailiwick is the most gallant and lovely of fishes. Once on a time, the Brule, like the Nipigon, was the home of — but I must omit the raptures.

About the native trout. The next morning I showed him to a fisherman. Cold and bright he was as I seized him from the refrigerator and held him up.

"Guess he'll go eighteen, eh?" I remarked.

The fisherman looked me straight in the eye and declared:

"Hell, he'll go twenty-two if he's an inch."

Gentlemen, there is the true manifestation of all that is praise worthy in an angler. That trout would have done well to pass sixteen inches!

In the interim between the first round and the next I hurriedly applied restoratives to Mr. McGinty. I brushed back his bedraggled wings. I rubbed his stomach. I let him rub his shoes in the rosin and whispered to him to work the old left hook. At the bell he was tired but dead game.

Nothing happened right away and I worked along rather fast for it was getting darker. There is a pool, a real pool, at this place, that fishermen call Rainbow Bend. It is deep and slow, with a slight surface ruffle in the center from the shaft

221

of current flowing into it.

McGinty, the embattled personification of some fly-tier's dream, landed at the head of the pool and there was enough slack in the line to let him reel groggily into the deeper water. The trout waiting for him must have thought he was punch drunk and ready for the haymaker, but McGinty came to life, and the counter punch he hung on that trout's jaw hooked the trout securely. The fish rallied, however, for he was as tough as McGinty and for the next five minutes he made me think I had hooked a big rainbow that had forgotten to return to the lake after the spring spawn.

He did not break water, but many big rainbows sometimes go the entire route without coming to the top, although it is usual for them to leap. Even the little dandiprats, four or five inches long, will leap like dolphins — only a lot faster and fiercer.

McGinty was compelled to do a lot of infighting in the second tussle, for the trout eventually got back into his own corner and for a few minutes he had the leader wrapped around something on the bottom. I waited to see if he would free himself, but finally risked everything on one jerk. McGinty remained with me and once more I had the trout out in open water and much more tired.

Once in the net I found him to be another native, and practically the same size as the first! I doubt if there was a difference of 1/2-inch in their length, and their weight was about the same. But poor McGinty — ah, McGinty, what they had done to you that evening! While he may have won both his fights by knockouts he looked anything but the smartly-colored little fellow that had pricked my finger as I groped for my own fly on the overhanging branch. His feathers were torn and tattered, his dashing vestments reduced to mere silk ravelings and his red tail was completely gone! The price of victory as ever, had been dear to McGinty on the Brule that evening. The path of glory was leading to the grave, no doubt about that, but McGinty still bore a resemblance to a trout fly and I sent him back to the wars.

I was traveling rapidly downstream by that time, in order to over take the ichthyological ingrate of my angling days, and the trout that saw McGinty reeling his way, a battered nondescript, without well defined mark or manner, tossed hurriedly into this pool and yanked summarily out of that pool, probably laughed at such artlessness. But McGinty, whose water-soaked togs were carrying him deeper and deeper, still had a scrap left in him, although he could not have been fighting under his true colors. He didn't have any more colors. I found out the old spirit was still there at the foot of a long series of rapids through which I had hastened. McGinty was sent forth into the tail of the last rapid and was joined in battle with lightning speed by a rainbow. No doubt about what kind of a trout he was. No feinting or clever footwork about that fellow. He simply struck and ducked, and as he did McGinty let go with the old left hook and his first punch was the beginning of the end. The rainbow proceeded to show me he was a match for any upstart Irishman and he writhed out of the water several times with McGinty hanging to him. It is not hard to envision him now, heaving skyward with nose straight up and body writhing. It was a sore test for McGinty, after the other two battles, but he was equal to the task. The rainbow was a pretty fish, somewhat shorter than the natives, but, perhaps, a trifle heavier.

But McGinty — poor McGinty.

What was left of his wings looked like water-soaked cobwebs. I lit a match to inspect the complete damage and found the hook even slightly bent outward. There had been a brave neck of hackle at the beginning. That was gone, or so confused with the remnants of wings as to be just the same as gone, and the body was worn and torn through so as to reveal the slender shank of the hook.

McGinty I carefully laid away between two felts to dry out and rest from his labors. He was in aristocratic company in the lid of that box, for many another fly had I wet or oiled before McGinty turned the tide. Handsome bivisibles, aristocratic fan-winged Coachmen, a glorified Parmacheene Belle, and a host of other plutocrats looked fine in the glow of the match but none so belligerently fine as McGinty as I reverently stuck him into the felt pad and snapped the cover shut.

Waiting at the car was the other fellow. He had seven, all

good fish, all caught on my McGinty — but none so large as my three.

"You can have four of 'em," he proffered.

His conscience was bothering him.

"What?" I cried. "Take another man's fish from him? I wouldn't do that any more than I'd take his last fly!"

Then I showed him my three and told him the story of McGinty's last stand.

"That's it," he declared. "Mine were all caught on the McGinty and you had to send it down to get results."

"I apologize for what I said about McGinty." I said. "He's a fightin' fool and deserves a lot of credit."

"It's the luck of the Irish," he replied. "It was simply McGinty's day to go down and he went down with a vengeance. Down went McGinty and up came Mr. Trout."

He was humming that as we backed out of the parking place and straightened away for home.

Mister President the teacher, MacQuarrie the pupil. MacQuarrie takes delight in this relationship. Mostly the inter- play comes as a form of banter or a vehicle for jokes but here the lesson has more bite.

He is making a point. This story appeared in 1937. The two men are fishing for smallmouth bass with their fly rods. Think of what bass fishing was like then. Few fished for bass (looked down on by trout fishermen anyway) with fly rods and poppers. Spinning tackle was unknown on these shores. The plastic worm (which started out as pork rind) wouldn't be dis- covered for almost twenty years. Tournaments were unheard of: The tackle of the era was a steel or bamboo bait casting rod, a reel whose handle spun when you cast it and plugs that weighed 5/8th of an ounce. Some are still classics. Heddon's River Runt. Creek Chub Pikie Minnow. Fred Arbogast's Hawaiian Wigglers.

Today, fly fishermen have discovered the game fighter which is the smallmouth. Ahead of the pack as usual, MacQuarrie says here, "Hey guys, try your fly rods on bass. It's great." And he goes to more than usual lengths to tell them how to do it.

If You Fish
The St. Croix

The President of the Old Duck Hunter's Association looked at me, and the light of battle was born in his eyes.

"I think," he said, "that you and I shall go bass fishing on the St. Croix."

That, of course, was a challenge. Mister President, by virtue of his office, presides at all meetings of this two-man association, and when I rose to a point of order he ruled me down. After all, maybe it was fair. But there lurked within me an unholy desire to show him that I had learned something about flies on trout streams; and by jinks, I would apply that knowledge on the St. Croix trip. He might choose the weapons, but I was not going to be caught unprepared.

So we went. There was a sinister foreboding in the demeanor of Mister President the morning we set forth. His customary affability was gone. His eyes snapped. He chewed two cigars to pieces on our way to the little bridge over the

St. Croix just below the place where the Moose River runs into it.

It was early July. The river looked good. Are there any clean rivers that ever look anything else but good? It seemed to me the fish therein ought to respond to my flies as well as the trout of other streams.

We guided the trailer down the bank and launched the green boat. I bent to the oars while Mister President unshipped a bait casting rod.

The deal called for one man being at the oars while the other fished. An hour on, an hour off. I was to take his orders first. He sent me upstream, underneath the bridge, alongside the pilings of the old lumber dam upon which the bridge had been built.

"Time was," said he, "when Joe Lynch and I used to catch the limit here in an hour or less."

"But times have changed," I ventured. He grunted something and sent a baby plug in close to the old piling.

"Take 'er slow here," he directed. "I want to stay right under the bridge for a while."

It was an awkward place in which to hold a boat, but I was there to obey orders. On about the twentieth cast a northern pike of three pounds hit the lure. It was soon over. Mister President methodically got out his pliers, the better to release the hooks, and then tossed the pike back.

"Hey!" I shouted in surprise. "You can't beat me that way."

If You Fish The St. Croix

"My boy," he said, rising to grandiloquent heights, "I am here to catch bass. I'll catch bass or nothing!"

A strange man — strange, indeed, especially in view of the fact that he and his wife actually prefer northern pike in the pan. And I agree on that too, which is of a piece with another alleged folly of mine that compels me to confess that I like codfish better than trout — in the pan, though, brother. Not on the end of my line!

"Work 'er upstream about fifty yards," ordered Mister President.

It was a relief to bend to the oars and get out of the gripping water where it narrowed under the bridge. During my hour at the sweeps I had to show some oarsmanship. The President demands good boating. He removed the little plug and snapped on a mousie.

"Beautiful thing," I remarked with the contempt that dry-fly fishermen are supposed to have for such frauds.

"I was right," murmured the President.

"What do you mean, you were right?"

"O.K. You asked for it. I'll give it to you. You're a trout fisher man — oh, just a helluva trout fisherman! You can float a fly. You can handle a curve cast fairly well. You know one bug from the other. You're pretty good. I admit it. Also, which is worse, you know it! Get me?"

"You've got to have confidence to catch 'em."

"Right you are — confidence. But how about that big chunk of cockiness that was sticking out of your hide that day on the Brule?"

"I didn't mean it that way."

"That's the way with you trout fishermen — especially you young ones. You get all buzzed up over trout. You dream about 'em at night. You throw your whole soul into the game. Their beauty, their fight, the classic methods used to catch them — all these things get you a little befuddled, and you begin to think no one ever went through that same process before. All that trout love happened to me twenty-five years ago.

There was truth in what he said. I knew I had been carried away by trout fishing. It had got to the point where I carried a thermometer and wrote to university professors to ask 'em about the life history of local bugs. He was handing me a rude awakening, but I accepted it, asking only the right to continue on a fair competitive basis. I still wanted to prove to him that trout and bass were sisters under their skins and that if I ever got away from those oars I'd show him.

After that outburst the President went to work. With lower lip stuck out in characteristic combativeness, he proceeded to work that part of the stream after the manner of a farmer raking hay in a drought year. Once in a while he muttered to himself. I couldn't hear, but I suspected he was making medicine for my confusion.

The first bass took a battered old minnow. This bass came out from under a rock fifty yards above the bridge, on

the left bank, right in front of a large log cabin on one of the biggest estates on the river. The President grunted and raised the tip of his battle-scarred rod. Every time the fish made a run Mister President would bite his tongue or stick out his undershot jaw.

The river is wide here. There are few underwater obstructions. He tired the bass in a few minutes, and I netted it. And when I felt that pound and a half of squirming bronze and black in the net bottom, it seemed to me the rainbows and brooks and browns were very, very far away. The bass' spines raised and lowered. His red-rimmed eyes stared back at me with "Trout fisherman, eh? Send around a rainbow about my size some day, and I'll knock him in half!"

The hour wasn't up yet. After that first fish, some of the President's anxiety was gone. He began to feel he had matters in hand. He leered at me a little bit; and when, at the foot of a rapids, two hundred yards above this bridge, he hooked another one of the same size, he turned around and crowed like a rooster.

And to show his versatility, now that he had his hand in, he rigged up his long-handled fly rod and bade me work the boat in close to the foot of the rapids. Working with a feather minnow, he laid it out over the gouged-out places below the rapids. At times, when one could hold the boat just right, it was possible to see four or five good-sized bass fanning just at the edge of the fast water, quite near the bottom.

If You Fish The St. Croix

They hardly stirred.

The President floated his lure at first, allowing the current to take full command. Nothing stirred. Then he placed it on slower water and manipulated it with teasing twitches. Almost immediately there was a swirl, but the fish missed. He did not rest this bass, as I would have done with a brown trout, but put the feather minnow right back in the same place and twitched it.

Zam! The President proved he was just as good with the fly rod as with the bait rod. This smallmouth got out into the fast water. Now there was no 14-pound-test line. No treble hooks to scarify the inside of the fish's mouth. He was held by a single hook, and he called his ally, the river current, to his aid. The fight was high, wide and handsome for fully five minutes before this chap came alongside and was swept into the net. There's something gallant about those redeyes. They don't quit, even in the net.

The President lit a cigarette, and as we changed seats I saw him grin at me from his place amidships. I put together my fly rod.

"Say where," said the President, at the oars.

"Right here," I decided.

We remained at the foot of the rapids. This was going to be easy, I decided, as my first cast — a floating feather shaped like a beetle — hit the water with a little spat. It was at the edge of the fast water, in moving water. It came down toward me fairly fast. I retrieved, surprised that nothing had hit it. Twenty casts yielded nothing. I was casting perfectly. There was no sign of drag. The bug looked like the goods to me. Then I tried the slower water at the edge. It floated right over the tops of those big fellows, fanning below. They didn't stir. I was beginning to feel a little foolish.

"Had enough?" asked the President at the end of a half hour of fruitless casting.

"Plenty," I confessed.

"All right," he replied. "Now take off that three-foot leader you tied on there, in your ignorance of bass wisdom. No, don't throw it away. Save it for tarpon, or muskies — or house-moving! Get out a 2X trout leader like I had — sure, seven feet long. Good! Try that."

I changed leaders obediently. It worked. In a few minutes one of those bass sidled up from the bottom and looked over my bass bug. I jerked it — maybe six inches. The bass slowly returned to his abode among the rocks. I saw him go. Mister President came to my rescue.

"Too much jerk on the rod," he advised. "You do the same thing with a wet fly on a trout stream. Take it easy. Just the tiniest little movement. Don't move the line or leader much in doing it. After all, you know, any sap can fish a dry fly, floating down right in front of him, long as he doesn't have to make it move without its being plain as day that something else moved it."

Try that one on your piano! Think upon it, you trout fishermen of the dry, floating persuasion. Can you make your fly move without showing much movement of line or leader? No, you can't, nor can anyone else, very well, but Mister President expects it to be done when bass fishing.

"Looka here," he said, and he was giving me cards and spades as he went on. "You fish with a dry trout fly. It's practically dead, far as you're concerned. If you figure out the currents right, so your line isn't lying in faster water than the fly, it'll float naturally, without drag. Now it's my experience bass don't go for such like. Sometimes, maybe. But usually they'll take a surface lure only when it seems to be alive and kicking. Wiser than trout? I don't know. But my guess is, their natural surface food is more likely to make a visible commotion in the water than, say, a natural trout fly.

"You ask me why I don't fish downstream and let the current do the job? Too much movement of the surface bug, fly or what-have-you. Fish against the current with a delicate hand, just moving your bug the tiniest little bit."

I did, for the rest of my hour, and caught one small bass.

"Anyway, you're learning," said the President as he squeezed by me at the end of the hour to take up his rod again.

I retired to the oars and ruminated upon this fishy discrepancy in which trout didn't demand a "kicking" surface lure and bass did. The thought was sinking in on me that bass may not be so dumb. I had known that some ultra-expert trout anglers had mastered a cast which put their fly on the water in a series of hops, but I could never learn that.

And maybe this moving it "ever so little" might be all right on trout!

"It should work," said the President, "but remember that 'ever so little'."

I watched. He ordered me back under the bridge and downstream a quarter of a mile. The water comes along here about two miles an hour. It is too deep for wading. I boated him down to the beginning of a series of rapids. We didn't want to run the rapids. The idea was to start at their head and work back up to the bridge.

"Enough good bass water within sight of this bridge to keep a fellow going all day," explained the President. He worked the right bank, putting his bass bugs in close to shore and letting the current have its way except for an occasional "twitch — not jerk," as he put it. Several little ones were hooked and put back. He changed to a larger bug — one I had found successful in night fishing for trout.

The sun was hitting in hard at that right bank. The left bank offered nothing — too shallow. It was obvious that the bass, if there were any, were beneath the undercut, deep right bank. He fished hard for his hour and took nothing but little ones. My turn came, and I couldn't even hook little ones.

But soon the sun dropped behind the elms and that promising right bank beckoned again. Back we went to the beginning of the rapids, and I returned to the oars for the final round. Mister President was getting his "last raps." He always does, and he'd certainly earned them that day. He adopted some new tactics — letting his bass bug hit the water with a splat. It came down quite hard. I had known this to be successful on night trout.

"If big bass are going to feed this evening, this ought to attract them," he explained. "Can't do this in the daytime, but it's different now."

He nailed one keeper before we were half-way back to the bridge.

"Just one more," he said, and he got it, too, not far from the bridge in that deep right-bank water. We pulled over toward the trailer and car. We had hardly been out of sight of it during that five hours' fishing. Gear was stowed. The little green boat was hauled up the bank through the brush and strapped to the trailer.

I was humbled. Mister President had seen to that. Ready to go, he lit a cigarette and gazed down the river into the dusky waters. The St. Croix gurgled along, disappearing in a left turn at the rapids below us, nearly a half mile away.

The President of the Old Duck Hunters' opened up and spoke his mind.

"You — I ain't gonna say anything to you about fishing. I don't have to. You learned something today. You learned there's more to fishing than getting cock-eyed crazy about one kind of it. Me, I'm just an old fisherman. I've read all the books like you and been through all the different crazy spells, including trout, muskies and lake trout. Now I'm getting old and mellow, like a keg of good whisky; and when someone tells me his particular fishing is the only kind, I'm inclined to set that man down as either a jackass or a very young fisherman. The only thing that saves you is your youth!"

It is time now to meet the new Mr. President. Not markedly different from the old Mr. President. Full of fun. Full of appreciation. Goodhearted. A boon companion.

Now I must throw a shadow over your thoughts. At the end of the tale, Mr. President bargains with what the author calls "The Sickle Man," declaring that if there are no guarantees in the hereafter of good trout and bass water, then "I ain't going." MacQuarrie could make no such bargain. This is the last story he ever wrote. It was published in 1957 after his death.

You Can't Take
It With You

The President of the Old Duck Hunters' Association finished his repast that Sabbath noon and his wife reminded him that the lawn needed mowing, one martin house had been tilted by the wind and the garden clamored to be weeded.

Mister President walked through the summer kitchen which held a freeze box of treasure, including trout, bass and walleyes. His fishing jacket and tackle were in a neat pile by the door leading to the back porch where the wild grapevine twined. He eschewed it.

He strode out on the back porch and looked across the street at the United States post office where he was postmaster and where he often started working at 6 A.M. and remained until midnight. For the hundredth time he thought it might be a good idea to sell the post office, a drastic measure which he often expounded on opening days to customers who approved of the idea hilariously.

243

Fly Fishing With MacQuarrie

Bob, the shorthair, and Becky, the springer, galloped up and awaited the word from their lord and master. Perhaps they knew what was passing through his mind. Bob's tail was violently in favor of truancy, for Bob is a direct actionist. Becky, more the opportunist, merely sat and hoped for the best.

Mister President disappointed them both. He took the lawn mower from the garage, lingering there only a few seconds to admire the sleek lines of a 16-foot canoe he was recovering with fiber glass. Within five minutes after the demon mower had begun to roar, three neighborhood urchins appeared from unknown crannies, looking for work, to which they were instantly put.

The three dandiprats, elevation about 40 inches, were signed on as horses, and Mister President explained that they were crossing the plains in a covered wagon and he was the wagon master.

"Gee-jap ... steady ... haw! Haw, you red-headed hoss! You wanna push the wagon and all our stores over the bank into the wide Missouri? ... Steady ... now, gee-jap."

The three hosses walked the mower up and down, halting occasionally on command of the wagon master to fall on their bellies and shoot it out with bands of Indian raiders.

A lady of considerable dignity, for such a pretty day, approached on the sidewalk.

"Sir!" She fixed the President with a fierce and righteous eye. "What do you mean by disturbing the Sabbath with this uproar?"

Heads poked cautiously out of nearby front doors and upper windows, for this lady was notorious in her determination to police the city of Mineral Point, Wisconsin, in the ways of Christianity as she saw them. The President of the Old Duck Hunters was not unequal to the occasion.

"Madam," he answered, "I plumb forgot it was Sunday, because I've been so damn busy minding my own business."

The lady went on her way, bloody, but unbowed, as screen doors closed softly and a little chorus of giggles floated from front porches beneath the 100-year-old elms. Above the roar of the mower, Mister President called out the marching orders:

"We'll make Alkali Bluff tonight, hosses. Plenty of grass and water for you there. Gee-jap."

The gallant hosses and/or Indian-fighting plainsmen had finished their strength-sapping labors and were ingesting fresh strawberries with thick cream — a quart apiece is the standard ration for all comers to this yard — when I drove my car up the short, steep driveway. The President flew into action.

"It's Geronimo and his band!" he cried. "Wheel the wagons into a circle and don't fire until you see the whites of their eyes."

The three plainsmen covered me with rifles that looked like Model 1873 Winchesters and fired white plastic balls. Mister President bravely directed the skirmish from behind a bowl of strawberries and cream —

"Shoot the hosses from under 'em, men. Then we'll tommyhawk 'em and scalp 'em when they're helpless on the ground!"

I advanced from my car waving a handkerchief on the middle section of a glass fly rod.

"Cease firing, men, the poor fellows are whupped."

Although I had recently dined, it was compulsory that I attack my portion of garden-fresh strawberries and cream. The three fighting men of the plains accepted additional helpings and sat there restuffing themselves, victorious and belching.

Mrs. President came out. She was about to cheer the billiard-table appearance of the lawn and saw me, so I had to accept another ladle of giant strawberries and impart the family news and amenities. Mister President volunteered:

"Now, Laura, he came all by himself all this way. Seems when I settle down to serious work somebody's always trying to lure me away."

The lady of his heart remarked that luring him away was about as difficult as persuading a rabbit to eat lettuce, and, for that matter, she would attend to the garden and straighten the martin house on its pole.

Mister President, by main force, imprisoned Becky and Bob in his own car to prevent them from following us, and as we backed down the driveway you could see them staring desperately at us through the rear window. At such a time you can hear a dog calling you unprintable names.

The smallmouth and trout domain we visited that day is part of the southwest corner of Wisconsin — the Driftless Area, as the geologists call it, where glaciers have never advanced or receded, and where a complete river system has been eroded by wind and rain and flowing water until the area is almost perfectly drained. A bucket of water thrown on the ground has only one way to go — downhill — looking for some other water.

In this land of the sky, so-called because hills are high and vistas are far, it has been estimated by Mister President that there are about a thousand miles of creeks and rivers which are predominantly smallmouth bass water, with some trout, especially browns in the upper reaches. I think his estimate is high but fear to challenge him, for he may add up that network of moving water to prove to me it's more than a thousand miles.

Our first stop was at the Fever River, not far from tiny Jenkinville. There we acquired a friend, Mr. Lyle "Fudge" Gates, straight as an arrow and merry as a meadowlark despite the burden of his 13 years. He was trying to catch a grasshopper and thus, eventually, a bass. In about four casts from the bank Mister President caught a 14-incher and presented it to Fudge with his compliments. Fudge took out for home on the dusty town road, clutching the giant to his ecstatic breast.

Gentlemen, I have had some awesome fishing in my

247

time. I have stood on the big boulders alongside the Clearwater River not far from where it leaves Careen Lake, Saskatchewan, and found it almost impossible not to take two grayling on every cast. In that same province I have fished with four others and often all five of us have had on, simultaneously, northerns in the neighborhood of 20 pounds.

And that is fine, just fine. But let me vouchsafe that the pure delight imparted that day to Mr. Fudge Gates by Mister President, with a little black bass from a rather muddy little stream, was strangely satisfying, and appropriate.

At this place the Fever winds through closely cropped pastures holding dairy herds and beef cattle. Banks are trampled and those same banks fairly cry out for someone to come and plant cover on them. But the smallmouths are there. At least they are every time I attend to the local rites with Mister President.

Protocol while fishing with Hizzoner in his own domain demands the use of his tested, proven spinner fly — solid black dressing, red head, slim white rubber streamer tonguing out below the single hook. The spinner will twirl in the least of currents. It is made from a light, white metal used by dentists and it is begged, borrowed or stolen from them for this purpose by the President of the Old Duck Hunters.

I recommend that black spinner fly without reservation. I have seen it, in various sizes, take muskies, northerns, walleyes, trout and bass. Far as I know it is nameless. A more imaginative angler than I would likely have named it long ago. Hizzoner evolved it over a period of years, and if I may speculate about its effectiveness, I would guess that its chief attraction is in that spinner, which whirls like a dervish if you so much as blow on it.

It's a meat-in-the-pan fly-rod lure. Possibly there is something important in that solid black dressing. At any rate,. one of the most successful of all the fly-rod men against the rainbows of the Douglas County Brule in Wisconsin was the late John Ziegler — and he put his faith in big, black bucktails.

Mister President, by his own admission, is a high-grader. He passes up a lot of water on those Driftless Area rivers. That means going from riffle to riffle and working the pools below the riffs. The process of high-grading brought a couple more smallmouths, and also Mr. Fudge Gates, who panted back to the streamside in time to get another bass a foot long and depart for home. We went along for the Grant River.

There's a place on this river where a gush of water leaps out of the limestone and falls 30 feet to the river. I stuck a thermometer into that flow and, though the air temperature was in the high 80s, the water was 54 degrees. It's colder than that in the ground, and that water, no doubt, is a solid reason why Brother Smallmouth tolerates the Driftless Area streams in spite of flash floods, silt and absence of bank cover.

It is surprising that so many miles of good smallmouth waters get so little pressure from anglers. The farmers in this opulent hill country hold down the bridges and the deep holes in an eternal quest for catfish. As for the bass angler, his work is easy. I wish it were harder, and it would be if those bald banks had only half the cover they need.

Mister President high-graded himself three more small-mouths within sight of that squirt of water from the lime-stone bluff above. He put them back, but said he'd save any-thing that got up to two pounds.

We moved along to the Platte River, to a place called King's Ford — high right bank, low left bank and the same surprisingly cold water from the limestone hill springs. Both of us picked up trout here — browns, 1/2-pounders — and these we saved. Like the bass, they were found in the holes below the riffs. They are not big enough to be called rapids.

On such days as this, the Old Duck Hunters are not averse to other charms of the Driftless Area. Short excursions into the box canyons along these valleys showed that the wild black raspberries were ripe and edible, that the blackberry crop would be a buster and that the wild grape tangles were bearing heavily after a year when the grapes were absent — and the ruffed grouse were not found at these favored tangles.

The area is dotted with wild crab apple trees. Each time I pass one I remember a day in brown October when the incorrigible Mister President paused before a tree loaded with red ripe crabs. He bit into one, smacked his lips, ate it, core and all.

"Honey crabs," he explained. "Sweetest apple this side of heaven."

Greedily I bit into one, though I should have known better. A more tasteless, a more bitter fruit has not touched the lips of man. How he ate one, for the sole purpose of getting a sucker like me merely to taste one, is something I shall never understand.

It was like chewing alum. And yet, Hizzoner, when he ate his, chewed and smacked and swallowed when his face should have been distorted and tears running down his cheeks. Hizzoner will go to great lengths for a laugh, but it takes a man of considerable will power to get 'em that way.

The Platte River was next, and when the dark began mounting up in the east we had two respectable smallmouths each, a brown trout each and some nice country to survey. We sat on a ledge of limestone and watched a farmer send his dog for the cows. A headstrong heifer sneaked away from the obedient herd, but her tawny nemesis brought her back with his teeth snapping close to her heels — "You do that again, sister, and I'll really bite you!"

No, not wilderness fishing. Not in the slightest. Pastoral is the word for it. No big fish to brag about. No heavy water to breast in waders. Just fishin' in nice country. The farmer whose dog rounded up the cows came over and sat on the limestone for a chat —

"I'll tell you, boys. You drop a good, stinky doughball into one of them holes and you're apt to get holt of the biggest dam' catfish this side the Mississippi."

It was all right with the Old Duck Hunters. Hizzoner figured it as an even split — "They get the catfish and we have the fun."

Quail scuttled across the gravelly town road as we pulled out of there and Mister President spoke of autumn days. "The grouse'll concentrate around those grape tangles again, sure's you're born." A considerate conservation commission apportions to this area the longest ruffed grouse season in Wisconsin, extending from mid-October to a few days before Christmas. Forget it if you haven't got a dependable dog, or those hills will murder you.

Within about six miles from home Mister President surmised, "She's probably got the garden weeded and the martin house fixed and it's still early." It was early, for a fisherman, not much after dark. He directed me to drive through a long, two-gate lane. We parked at the end of it and walked about a quarter of a mile through deep grass to the headwaters of what can be nothing but a feeder of the Pecatonica River.

That is all I can say about this place. If it has a name, Hizzoner did not tell me, although I prodded him a few times, just gently. I have found it profitable not to attempt to trespass into the mind of a fisherman.

You Can't Take It With You

The stream here was slight, with little widespreads and like the others we had seen that day, largely devoid of bank cover. A fine place for the casting of the night line with a fly rod. Mister President vanished in the dark upstream, and I combed the nearby waters for almost an hour with no luck.

I was at the car waiting for him when he came through the high grass to the lane. He dropped a brown of about three pounds on the floor of the car. "There's browns in there big enough to swallow that one."

Becky and Bob began a two-dog riot when the car burst up the short, steep driveway. Hizzoner quieted them hurriedly. He opened the garden gate and made a swift appraisal. "Not a weed in sight," he whispered. He went to the martin house pole and squinted upward. "Straight as a string."

The back porch light flicked on and the Old Duck Hunters were summoned to sit at a table arranged there of fried chicken and fearsome quantities of strawberries. Any number of people who have been entrapped on that back porch in the strawberry season can testify that when they leave they can be picked up and bounced, like a basketball.

Hizzoner lay back in a porch chair and contemplated the night through the grapevine leaves. Becky and Bob came close, the better to adore him. He sighed.

"Laura," he said, "I can probably find time tomorrow after work to weed the garden and straighten the martin house."

She said, "Huh!" She added succinct and appropriate remarks, for the time was opportune, but I noticed that she mussed his hair and smiled the smile of a wise woman before she left us alone on the porch.

We spoke of the country we had seen. I suggested he should consider himself lucky to be living in the midst of it, but, said I, there would come a day when the old geezer with the big sickle would come along and put an end to our days.

Mister President, challenged, sat bolt upright in his chair.

"Let him come," said he. "I've got to have a guarantee from him that he's got some trout and bass water up there in the big yonder — yes, and some first-rate grouse cover and some duck hunting."

"You can't take it with you," I said, which was indeed the obvious reply to this man challenging fate. "Nor, can you send it on ahead. What are you going to do if the Sickle Man tells you he will not bargain?"

There was nothing obvious in the reply that the President of the Old Duck Hunters snapped at me.

"In that case, I ain't going."